Mission Praise

Compiled by
Peter Horrobin and Greg Leavers

MUSICIANS' EDITION
VOLUME 3
537 – 798

Marshall Pickering

William Collins Sons & Co. Ltd.
London · Glasgow · Sydney · Auckland
Toronto · Johannesburg

First published in Great Britain in 1990 by Marshall Pickering

Marshall Pickering is an imprint of
Collins Religious Division,
part of the Collins Publishing Group
8 Grafton Street, London W1X 3LA

Compilation copyright © 1990 Peter Horrobin, Greg Leavers
and London and Nationwide Missions

Music and text set by Barnes Music Engraving Ltd, East Sussex, England
Printed in Great Britain by Martins of Berwick

ISBN 0 551 02268 X

Music Edition   ISBN 0 551 01986 7

Words Edition   ISBN 0 551 01979 4 (Single copy)
                       ISBN 0 551 01977 8 (Pack of 25)
Large Print
  Words Edition   ISBN 0 551 01978 6

Musicians' Edition vol. 1 ISBN 0 551 02266 3
              vol. 2 ISBN 0 551 02267 1
                      ISBN 0 551 02313 9 (Pack of three volumes)

Preface

This combined volume of Mission Praise brings together the original volume that was compiled for Mission England with the second and supplementary volumes. The contents of these three books, with the addition of some extra items, and now numbering 798 songs, has been structured so as to be a comprehensive hymn and song book for church and general use.

The success of Mission Praise owes much to its strategy of embracing the best of the old with the best of the new, freely mixing together both traditional hymns and modern songs. As such the volumes have gained wide acceptance with all ages and, indeed, a very wide range of church congregations.

The large and comprehensive subject and music indexes will be an invaluable aid to the selection of items for use throughout the church's year, at all special events in church and family life and for other special services.

The vision for the original Mission Praise volume eventually extended far beyond our initial expectations, and we give thanks to God for the way in which the collection opened up major new dimensions of praise and worship in many churches. Our prayer for this combined edition is that the blessings enjoyed by those who used the first volume of Mission Praise will be shared by all who use this combined volume.

Peter Horrobin and Greg Leavers

537 On Christmas night

SUSSEX CAROL 88 88 88

Words: Traditional
Music: English traditional melody
arranged R Vaughan Williams (1872–1958)

On Christ-mas night all Christ-ians sing to hear the news_ the

an-gels bring: on Christ-mas night all Christ-ians sing to

hear the news the an-gels bring: news of great joy,_ news of_ great

mirth, news of our mer-ci-ful_ King's birth.

Music arrangement: © Stainer & Bell Ltd,
PO Box 110, 82 High Road, London N2 9PW

1 On Christmas night all Christians sing
to hear the news the angels bring:
on Christmas night all Christians sing
to hear the news the angels bring:
news of great joy, news of great mirth,
news of our merciful King's birth.

2 Then why should we on earth be so sad,
since our Redeemer made us glad,
then why should we on earth be so sad,
since our Redeemer made us glad,
when from our sin He set us free,
all for to gain our liberty?

3 When sin departs before His grace,
then life and health come in its place;
when sin departs before His grace,
then life and health come in its place;
angels and men with joy may sing,
all for to see the new-born King.

4 All out of darkness we have light,
which made the angels sing this night:
all out of darkness we have light,
which made the angels sing this night:
'Glory to God and peace to men,
now and for evermore. Amen.'

538 On Jordan's bank, the Baptist's cry

WINCHESTER NEW   LM

Words: Charles Coffin (1676–1749)
tr. John Chandler (1806–76)
altered Horrobin/Leavers
Music: adapted from a chorale in
Musicalisches Hand-Buch, Hamburg, 1690
arranged W H Havergal (1793–1870)

On Jor-dan's bank the___ Bap-tist's cry an-noun-ces___ that the Lord is nigh; come then and___ list-en___ for___ he___ brings glad tid-ings from the King of kings.

1 On Jordan's bank the Baptist's cry
announces that the Lord is nigh;
come then and listen for he brings
glad tidings from the King of kings.

2 Then cleansed be every heart from sin;
make straight the way for God within;
prepare we in our hearts a home,
where such a mighty guest may come.

3 For You are our salvation, Lord,
our refuge and our great reward;
without Your grace we waste away,
like flowers that wither and decay.

4 To heal the sick stretch out Your hand,
make wholeness flow at Your command;
sin's devastation now restore
earth's own true loveliness once more.

5 To Him who left the throne of heaven
to save mankind, all praise be given;
to God the Father, voices raise,
and Holy Spirit, let us praise.

539 Once in royal David's city

IRBY   87 87 77

Words: Cecil Frances Alexander (1823–95)
altered Horrobin/Leavers
Music: Henry John Gauntlett (1805–76)

Once in roy-al Da-vid's__ ci-ty, stood a low-ly cat-tle__ shed, where a mo-ther laid__ her__ ba-by, in a man-ger for__ His__ bed. Ma-ry__ was__ that mo-ther mild, Je-sus__ Christ__ her lit-tle__ child.

1 Once in royal David's city,
   stood a lowly cattle shed,
   where a mother laid her baby,
   in a manger for His bed.
   Mary was that mother mild,
   Jesus Christ her little child.

2 He came down to earth from heaven,
   who is God and Lord of all;
   and His shelter was a stable,
   and His cradle was a stall:
   with the poor and mean and lowly
   lived on earth our Saviour holy.

3 And through all His wondrous childhood
   He would honour and obey,
   love, and watch the lowly mother,
   in whose gentle arms He lay:
   Christian children all should be,
   kind, obedient, good as He.

4 For He is our childhood's pattern:
   day by day like us He grew;
   He was little, weak, and helpless,
   tears and smiles like us He knew;
   and He feels for all our sadness,
   and He shares in all our gladness.

5 And our eyes at last shall see Him,
   through His own redeeming love;
   for that child, so dear and gentle,
   is our Lord in heaven above;
   and He leads His children on
   to the place where He is gone.

6 Not in that poor lowly stable,
   with the oxen standing by,
   we shall see Him, but in heaven,
   set at God's right hand on high;
   there His children gather round,
   bright like stars, with glory crowned.

540

One day when heaven

Words: J Wilbur Chapman (1859–1918)
Music: Charles H Marsh

One day when hea - ven was filled with His prais - es, one day when
sin was as black as could be,___ Je-sus came forth to be born of a
vir - gin, dwelt a-mongst men, my ex-am-ple is He!___
Liv-ing, He loved me; dy-ing, He saved me; bur-ied, He

car - ried my sins far a - way,___ ris-ing, He jus - ti-fied free-ly for
ev - er: one day He's com - ing: O glo - ri - ous day.___

1 One day when heaven was filled with His praises,
one day when sin was as black as could be,
Jesus came forth to be born of a virgin,
dwelt amongst men, my example is He!
  Living, He loved me; dying, He saved me;
  buried, He carried my sins far away,
  rising, He justified freely for ever:
  one day He's coming: O glorious day.

2 One day they led Him up Calvary's mountain,
one day they nailed Him to die on the tree;
suffering anguish, despised and rejected;
bearing our sins, my Redeemer is He!
  Living, He loved me . . .

3 One day they left Him alone in the garden,
one day He rested, from suffering free;
angels came down o'er His tomb to keep vigil;
hope of the hopeless, my Saviour is He!
  Living, He loved me . . .

4 One day the grave could conceal Him no longer,
one day the stone rolled away from the door;
Then He arose, over death He had conquered;
now is ascended, my Lord evermore!
  Living, He loved me . . .

5 One day the trumpet will sound for His coming,
one day the skies with His glory will shine;
wonderful day, my beloved ones bringing;
glorious Saviour, this Jesus is mine!
  Living, He loved me . . .

541 One shall tell another

Words and music: Graham Kendrick
Music arranged Christopher Norton

Lightly with increasing pace

One shall tell an - oth - er, and he shall tell his friends,

hus-bands, wives and child-ren shall come fol-low-ing on. From

house to house in fa - mi - lies shall more be gath-ered in; and

lights will shine in ev-ery street, so warm and wel-com - ing.

Come on in___ and taste the new wine, *the wine of the king-dom,*

1 One shall tell another,
  and he shall tell his friends,
  husbands, wives and children
  shall come following on.
  From house to house in families
  shall more be gathered in;
  and lights will shine in every street,
  so warm and welcoming.
    Come on in
    and taste the new wine,
    the wine of the kingdom,
    the wine of the kingdom of God:
    here is healing and forgiveness,
    the wine of the kingdom,
    the wine of the kingdom of God.

2 Compassion of the Father
  is ready now to flow;
  through acts of love and mercy
  we must let it show.
  He turns now from His anger
  to show a smiling face,
  and longs that men should stand beneath
  the fountain of His grace.
    Come on in . . .

3 He longs to do much more than
  our faith has yet allowed,
  to thrill us and suprise us
  with His sovereign power.
  Where darkness has been darkest,
  the brightest light will shine;
  His invitation comes to us –
  it's yours and it is mine.
    Come on in . . .

542   One there is, above all others

GOUNOD   87 87 77

Words: John Newton (1725–1807)
Music: Charles Gounod (1818–93)

One there is, a - bove all oth - ers, well de - serves the_ name of friend; His is love be - yond_ a_ bro - ther's, cost - ly, free, and_ knows no end: they who once His_ kind - ness prove, find it ev - er - last - ing love.

1 One there is, above all others,
  well deserves the name of friend;
His is love beyond a brother's,
  costly, free, and knows no end:
they who once His kindness prove,
find it everlasting love.

2 Which of all our friends, to save us,
  could, or would, have shed His blood?
Christ, the Saviour, died to have us
  reconciled in Him to God:
this was boundless love indeed!
Jesus is a friend in need.

3 When He lived on earth abasèd,
  'Friend of sinners' was His name;
now, above all glory raisèd,
  He rejoices in the same:
still He calls them brethren, friends,
and to all their wants attends.

4 O for grace our hearts to soften!
  teach us, Lord, at length to love.
We, alas! forget too often
  what a friend we have above:
but when home our souls are brought,
we will love Thee as we ought.

543 Onward Christian soldiers

St Gertrude   65 65 D with refrain

Words: S Baring-Gould (1834–1924)
Music: Arthur S Sullivan (1842–1900)

On-ward Christ-ian sol - diers, march-ing as to war,
with the cross of Je - sus go-ing on be - fore.
Christ the roy - al Mas - ter leads a - gainst the foe;
for-ward in - to bat - tle,___ see, His ban-ners go!

1 Onward Christian soldiers, marching as to war,
   with the cross of Jesus going on before.
   Christ the royal Master leads against the foe;
   forward into battle, see, His banners go!
   Onward, Christian soldiers, marching as to war,
   with the cross of Jesus going on before.

2 At the name of Jesus Satan's legions flee;
   on then, Christian soldiers, on to victory.
   Hell's foundations quiver at the shout of praise;
   brothers, lift your voices, loud your anthems raise.
   Onward, Christian soldiers . . .

3 Like a mighty army moves the Church of God;
   brothers, we are treading where the saints have trod;
   we are not divided, all one body we,
   one in hope and calling, one in charity.
   Onward, Christian soldiers . . .

4 Crowns and thrones may perish, kingdoms rise and wane,
   but the Church of Jesus constant will remain;
   gates of hell can never 'gainst that Church prevail;
   We have Christ's own promise, and that cannot fail.
   Onward, Christian soldiers . . .

5 Onward, then, ye people, join our happy throng,
   blend with ours your voices in the triumph song;
   glory, praise and honour unto Christ the King;
   This through countless ages men and angels sing.
   Onward, Christian soldiers . . .

544　Open my eyes that I may see

OPEN MY EYES　Irregular

Words and music: Clara Scott (1841–97)
Music arranged Fred P Morris

O-pen my eyes that I may see glimp-ses of truth Thou
hast for me; place in my hands the won-der-ful key
that shall un-clasp and set me free. Si-lent-ly now I
wait for Thee, rea-dy, my God, Thy will to see;

o - pen my eyes, il - lu - mine me, Spi - rit di - vine!___

1 Open my eyes that I may see
   glimpses of truth Thou hast for me;
   place in my hands the wonderful key
   that shall unclasp and set me free.
      Silently now I wait for Thee,
      ready, my God, Thy will to see;
      open my eyes, illumine me,
      Spirit divine!

2 Open my ears that I may hear
   voices of truth Thou sendest clear;
   and while the wave-notes fall on my ear,
   everything false will disappear.
      Silently now I wait . . .

3 Open my mouth and let me bear
   tidings of mercy everywhere;
   open my heart and let me prepare
   love with Thy children thus to share.
      Silently now I wait . . .

4 Open my mind, that I may read
   more of Thy love in word and deed:
   what shall I fear while yet Thou dost lead?
   Only for light from Thee I plead.
      Silently now I wait . . .

545

Open our eyes, Lord

Words and music: Robert Cull
Music arranged David Peacock

546

Open Thou mine eyes

From Psalm 119
Words and music: C C Kerr

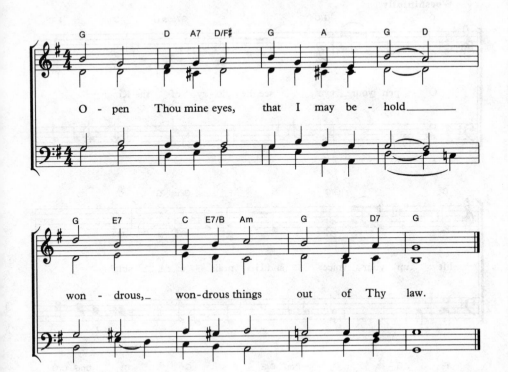

O - pen Thou mine eyes, that I may be - hold_____

won - drous,__ won-drous things out of Thy law.

547 Open your eyes

Words and music: Carl Tuttle
Music arranged Christopher Norton

Worshipfully

O - pen your eyes, see the glo - ry of the King;

lift up your voice, and His prais - es sing!

I love You, Lord, I will pro-claim:

Al - le - lu - ia! I bless Your name.

548 Our blest Redeemer

St Cuthbert 86 84

Words: Henriette Auber (1773–1862)
Music: John Bacchus Dykes (1823–76)

Our blest Re-deem-er, ere He breathed His ten-der last fare-well,

a guide, a com-fort-er be-queathed, with us to dwell.

1 Our blest Redeemer, ere He breathed
His tender last farewell,
a guide, a comforter bequeathed,
with us to dwell.

2 He came in semblance of a dove,
with sheltering wings outspread,
the holy balm of peace and love
on earth to shed.

3 He came in tongues of living flame,
to teach, convince, subdue;
all powerful as the wind He came,
as viewless too.

4 He comes sweet influence to impart,
a gracious, willing guest,
where He can find one humble heart
wherein to rest.

5 And His that gentle voice we hear,
soft as the breath of even,
that checks each fault, that calms each fear,
and speaks of heaven.

6 And every virtue we possess,
and every victory won,
and every thought of holiness,
are His alone.

7 Spirit of purity and grace,
our weakness, pitying, see;
O make our hearts Thy dwelling-place,
and worthier Thee.

549 Our eyes have seen the glory

Words: Roland Meredith
Music: American traditional melody
arranged Phil Burt

- lu - jah, glo - ry, glo - ry hal - le - lu - jah,
glo - ry, glo - ry hal - le - lu - jah, all hail as - cend - ed King! ___

1 Our eyes have seen the glory
of our Saviour, Christ the Lord;
He is seated at His Father's side
in love and full accord;
from there upon the sons of men
His Spirit is out-poured,
all hail, ascended King!
Glory, glory hallelujah,
glory, glory hallelujah,
glory, glory hallelujah,
all hail ascended King!

2 He came to earth at Christmas
and was made a man like us;
He taught, He healed, He suffered –
and they nailed Him to the cross;
He rose again on Easter Day –
our Lord victorious,
all hail, ascended King!
Glory, glory . . .

3 The good news of His kingdom
must be preached to every shore,
the news of peace and pardon,
and the end of strife and war;
the secret of His kingdom
is to serve Him evermore,
all hail, ascended King!
Glory, glory . . .

4 His kingdom is a family
of men of every race,
they live their lives in harmony,
enabled by His grace;
they follow His example
till they see Him face to face,
all hail, ascended King!
Glory, glory . . .

550 Our Father in heaven

Words: from *The Alternative Service Book 1980*
Music: John Marsh

551

Out of my bondage

JESUS, I COME   Irregular

Words: W T Sleeper (1840–1920)
Music: George C Stebbins (1846–1945)

Out of my bond-age, sor-row, and night, Je-sus, I come:

Je-sus, I come; in - to Your free - dom, glad-ness, and light,

Je-sus, I come to You.— Out of my sick-ness in - to Your health,

out of my want and in - to Your wealth, out of my sin and

in - to Your-self, Je - sus, I come to You.

1 Out of my bondage, sorrow, and night,
Jesus, I come: Jesus, I come;
into Your freedom, gladness, and light,
Jesus, I come to You.
Out of my sickness into Your health,
out of my want and into Your wealth,
out of my sin and into Yourself,
Jesus, I come to You.

2 Out of my shameful failure and loss,
Jesus, I come: Jesus, I come;
into the glorious gain of Your cross,
Jesus, I come to You.
Out of earth's sorrows into Your balm,
out of life's storm and into Your calm,
out of distress to jubilant psalm,
Jesus, I come to You.

3 Out of unrest and arrogant pride,
Jesus, I come: Jesus, I come;
into Your blessèd will to abide,
Jesus, I come to You.
Out of myself to dwell in Your love,
out of despair into joy from above,
upward for ever on wings like a dove,
Jesus, I come to You.

4 Out of the fear and dread of the tomb,
Jesus, I come: Jesus, I come;
into the joy and light of Your home,
Jesus, I come to You.
Out of the depths of ruin untold,
into the peace of Your sheltering fold,
ever Your glorious face to behold,
Jesus, I come to You.

552 Our Father who is in heaven

CARIBBEAN LORD'S PRAYER   Music arrangement: Allen Percival

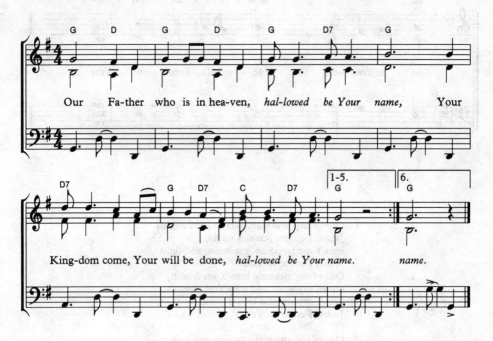

Our Fa-ther who is in hea-ven, *hal-lowed be Your name,* Your King-dom come, Your will be done, *hal-lowed be Your name.* name.

1 Our Father who is in heaven,
   hallowed be Your name,
   Your Kingdom come, Your will be done,
   hallowed be Your name.

2 On earth as it is in heaven,
   hallowed be Your name,
   give us this day our daily bread,
   hallowed be Your name.

3 Forgive us all our trespasses,
   hallowed be Your name,
   as we forgive those who trespass against us,
   hallowed be Your name.

4 And lead us not into temptation,
   hallowed be Your name,
   but deliver us from all that is evil,
   hallowed be Your name.

5 For Yours is the Kingdom, the Power and the Glory,
   hallowed be Your name,
   for ever and for ever,
   hallowed be Your name.

6 Amen, amen, it shall be so,
   hallowed be Your name,
   amen, amen, it shall be so,
   hallowed be Your name.

553 Peace I give to you

Words and music: Graham Kendrick
Music arranged Christopher Norton

1 Peace I give to you, I give to you My peace;
peace I give to you, I give to you My peace.
Let it flow to one another,
let it flow, let it flow;
let it flow to one another,
let it flow, let it flow.

2 Love I give to you, I give to you My love;
love I give to you, I give to you My love.
Let it flow . . .

3 Hope I give to you, I give to you My hope;
hope I give to you, I give to you My hope.
Let it flow . . .

4 Joy I give to you, I give to you My joy;
joy I give to you, I give to you My joy.
Let it flow . . .

Words and music: © 1979 Make Way Music,
administered in Europe by Thankyou Music,
PO Box 75, Eastbourne, East Sussex BN23 6NW, UK

554 Peace is flowing like a river

Words and music: Anon
Music arranged Betty Pulkingham

Peace is flow-ing like a riv - er,
flow - ing out through you and me,
spread - ing out in - to the des - ert,
set - ting all the cap-tives free, set - ting all the cap-tives free.

Love is flowing . . .
Joy is flowing . . .
Faith is flowing . . .
Hope is flowing . . . *etc.*

555(i)   Peace, perfect peace

PAX TECUM   10 10

Words: E H Bickersteth (1825–1906)
Music: George Thomas Calbeck (1852–1918)
and Charles Vincent (1852–1934)

1   Peace, perfect peace, in this dark world of sin?
The blood of Jesus whispers peace within.

2   Peace, perfect peace, by thronging duties pressed?
To do the will of Jesus, this is rest.

3   Peace, perfect peace, with sorrows surging round?
In Jesus' presence nought but calm is found.

4   Peace, perfect peace, with loved ones far away?
In Jesus' keeping we are safe, and they.

5   Peace, perfect peace, our future all unknown?
Jesus we know, and He is on the throne.

6   Peace, perfect peace, death shadowing us and ours?
Jesus has vanquished death and all its powers.

7   It is enough: earth's struggles soon shall cease,
and Jesus call us to heaven's perfect peace.

555(ii) Peace, perfect peace

Song 46   10 10

Words: E H Bickersteth (1825–1906)
Music: Orlando Gibbons (1583–1625)

1 Peace, perfect peace, in this dark world of sin?
   The blood of Jesus whispers peace within.

2 Peace, perfect peace, by thronging duties pressed?
   To do the will of Jesus, this is rest.

3 Peace, perfect peace, with sorrows surging round?
   In Jesus' presence nought but calm is found.

4 Peace, perfect peace, with loved ones far away?
   In Jesus' keeping we are safe, and they.

5 Peace, perfect peace, our future all unknown?
   Jesus we know, and He is on the throne.

6 Peace, perfect peace, death shadowing us and ours?
   Jesus has vanquished death and all its powers.

7 It is enough: earth's struggles soon shall cease,
   and Jesus call us to heaven's perfect peace.

556 Peace to you

Words and music: Graham Kendrick

Peace to you, We bless you now— in the name of the

Lord, Peace to you. We bless you now— in the name of the

Prince of Peace. Peace to you, peace to

you, peace to you, peace to you.

557   Praise God

Words: Thomas Ken (1637–1710)
Music: Jimmy Owens

Praise God from whom all bless - ings flow; praise Him all crea - tures here be - low, praise Him a - bove ye hea - ven - ly hosts; praise Fa - ther, Son, and Ho - ly Ghost.

Optional 4-part setting

Praise God___ from whom all bless - ings flow; praise

Him___ all crea - tures here___ be - low, praise

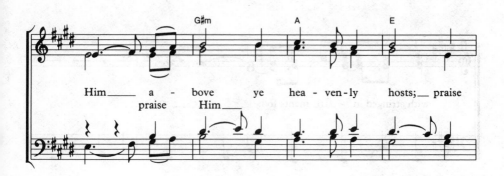

Him___ a - bove ye hea - ven-ly hosts;___ praise
praise Him___

Fa - ther, Son,___ and Ho - ly Ghost. Praise. Ghost.

558 Praise Him on the trumpet

Words and music: John Kennett
Music arranged Christopher Norton

8va bassa

559 Praise Him, praise Him

PRAISE HIM!   12 10 12 10 11 10 12 10

Words: Frances van Alstyne (1820–1915)
(Fanny J Crosby)
Music: C G Allen (1838–78)

1 Praise Him, praise Him! Je-sus, our bless-ed Re - deem - er!
2 Praise Him, praise Him! Je-sus, our bless-ed Re - deem - er!
3 Praise Him, praise Him! Je-sus, our bless-ed Re - deem - er!

Sing, O earth–His won-der-ful love pro - claim!
for our sins He suf-fered, and bled, and died;
heaven-ly por-tals, loud with ho-san-nas ring!

Hail Him, hail Him! high-est arch-an-gels in glo - ry;
He - our rock, our hope of e-ter-nal sal-va - tion,
Je - sus, Sav - iour, reign-eth for ev-er and ev - er:

strength and hon - our give to his ho - ly name!
hail Him, hail Him! Je - sus the cru - ci - fied!
crown Him, crown Him! Pro-phet, and Priest, and King!

560 Praise, my soul, the King of heaven

PRAISE, MY SOUL   87 87 87

Words: H F Lyte (1793–1847)
Music: J Goss (1800–80)

Praise Him! Praise the__ ev - er - last - ing__ King.

1 Praise, my soul, the King of heaven;
to His feet thy tribute bring;
ransomed, healed, restored, forgiven,
who like thee His praise should sing?
Praise Him! Praise Him!
Praise Him! Praise Him!
Praise the everlasting King.

2 Praise Him for His grace and favour
to our fathers, in distress;
praise Him still the same for ever,
slow to chide, and swift to bless.
Praise Him! Praise Him!
Praise Him! Praise Him!
Glorious in His faithfulness.

3 Father-like He tends and spares us;
well our feeble frame He knows;
in His hands He gently bears us,
rescues us from all our foes.
Praise Him! Praise Him!
Praise Him! Praise Him!
Widely as His mercy flows.

4 Angels help us to adore Him;
ye behold Him face to face;
sun and moon, bow down before Him;
dwellers all in time and space.
Praise Him! Praise Him!
Praise Him! Praise Him!
Praise with us the God of grace.

561 Praise the Lord

From Psalm 150
Words and music:
Lee Abbey Music Workshop

From *Sing Good News No 1*

562 Praise the Lord

Words and music: David J Hadden

praise Him with the harp and lyre,_____

praise Him with the tam-bour-ine_ and with danc - ing;_____ let

ev-ery-thing_ that has breath praise the Lord.

Praise the Lord,
praise God in His sanctuary,
praise Him in His mighty heavens;
praise Him for His greatness,
and praise Him for His power.
Praise the Lord . . .

1 Praise Him with the sound of trumpets,
   praise Him with the harp and lyre,
   praise Him with the tambourine and with dancing;
   let everything that has breath praise the Lord.
     Praise the Lord . . .

2 Praise Him with the clash of cymbals,
   praise Him with the strings and flute,
   praise Him with the tambourine and with dancing;
   let everything that has breath praise the Lord.
     Praise the Lord . . .

563

Praise to the Holiest

GERONTIUS CM

Words: J H Newman (1801–90)
Music J B Dykes (1823–76)

1 Praise to the Holiest in the height,
and in the depth be praise;
in all His words most wonderful;
most sure in all His ways.

2 O loving wisdom of our God!
when all was sin and shame,
a second Adam to the fight,
and to the rescue came.

3 O wisest love! that flesh and blood
which did in Adam fail,
should strive afresh against the foe,
should strive and should prevail.

4 And that a higher gift than grace
should flesh and blood refine,
God's presence, and His very self
and essence all-divine.

5 O generous love! that He, who smote
in Man for man the foe,
the double agony in Man
for man should undergo.

6 And in the garden secretly,
and on the cross on high,
should teach His brethren, and inspire
to suffer and to die.

7 Praise to the Holiest in the height
and in the depth be praise:
in all His words most wonderful;
most sure in all His ways.

564
Praise to the Lord

LOBE DEN HERREN   14 14 47 8

Words: Joachim Neander (1650–80)
tr. Catherine Winkworth (1829–78)
Music: from *Stralsund Gesangbuch*, 1665

Praise to the Lord, the Al - migh - ty, the King of cre -

- a - - tion; O my soul, praise Him, for He is thy

health and sal - va - tion; all ye who hear, bro-thers and

sis - ters, draw near, praise Him in glad a - do - ra - tion.

1 Praise to the Lord, the Almighty, the King of creation;
   O my soul, praise Him, for He is thy health and salvation;
   all ye who hear,
   brothers and sisters, draw near,
   praise Him in glad adoration.

2 Praise to the Lord, who o'er all things so wondrously reigneth,
   shelters thee under His wings, yea, so gently sustaineth:
   hast thou not seen?
   all that is needful hath been
   granted in what He ordaineth.

3 Praise to the Lord, who doth prosper thy work, and defend thee!
   surely His goodness and mercy here daily attend thee.
   Ponder anew
   what the Almighty can do,
   who with His love doth befriend thee.

4 Praise to the Lord! O let all that is in me adore Him!
   All that hath life and breath come now with praises before Him!
   Let the Amen
   sound from His people again:
   gladly for aye we adore Him.

565

Praise You, Lord

Words and music: Nettie Rose
Music arranged Christopher Norton

Praise You, Lord, for the won-der of Your heal-ing; praise You, Lord, for Your love so free-ly given; out-pour-ing, a-noint-ing, flow-ing in to heal our wounds—

praise You,— Lord, for Your love for———— me.

1 Praise You, Lord,
   for the wonder of Your healing;
   praise You, Lord,
   for Your love so freely given;
   out-pouring, anointing,
   flowing in to heal our wounds –
   praise You, Lord,
   for Your love for me.

2 Praise You, Lord,
   for Your gift of liberation;
   praise You, Lord,
   You have set the captives free;
   the chains that bind are broken
   by the sharpness of Your sword –
   praise You, Lord,
   You gave Your life for me.

3 Praise You, Lord,
   You have borne the depths of sorrow;
   praise You, Lord,
   for Your anguish on the tree;
   the nails that tore Your body
   and the pain that tore Your soul –
   praise You, Lord,
   Your tears, they fell for me.

4 Praise You, Lord,
   You have turned our thorns to roses;
   glory, Lord, as they bloom upon Your brow;
   the path of pain is hallowed,
   for Your love has made it sweet –
   praise You, Lord,
   and may I love You now.

566   Praise the name of Jesus

Words and music: Roy Hicks

Praise the name of Je - sus, Praise the name of
Je - sus, He's my rock, He's my fort - ress,
He's my de - liv - er - er, in Him will I trust;
Praise the name of Je - sus.

567 Prayer is the soul's sincere desire

NOX PRAECESSIT   CM

Words: James Montgomery (1771–1854)
Music: J Baptiste Calkin (1827–1905)

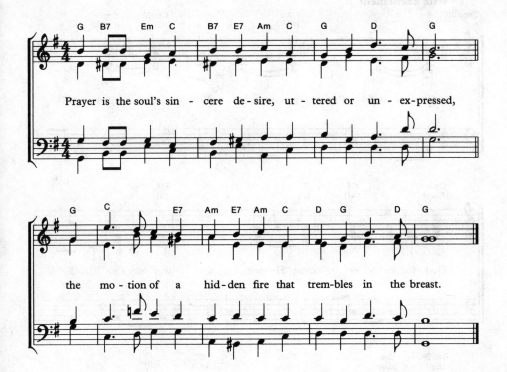

Prayer is the soul's sin - cere de-sire, ut - tered or un - ex-pressed,

the mo - tion of a hid-den fire that trem-bles in the breast.

1 Prayer is the soul's sincere desire,
uttered or unexpressed,
the motion of a hidden fire
that trembles in the breast.

2 Prayer is the burden of a sigh,
the falling of a tear,
the upward glancing of an eye,
when none but God is near.

3 Prayer is the simplest form of speech
that infant lips can try;
prayer the sublimest strains that reach
the majesty on high.

4 Prayer is the contrite sinner's voice,
returning from his ways;
while angels in their songs rejoice,
and cry, 'Behold, he prays!'

5 Prayer is the Christian's vital breath,
the Christian's native air,
his watchword at the gates of death;
he enters heaven with prayer.

6 No prayer is made on earth alone;
the Holy Spirit pleads;
and Jesus on the eternal throne,
for sinners intercedes.

7 O Thou by whom we come to God,
the life, the truth, the way,
the path of prayer Thyself hast trod;
Lord, teach us how to pray!

568 Reconciled

Words and music: Mike Kerry

With excitement

Re-con-ciled, I'm re-con-ciled, I'm re-con-ciled to God for ev - er; know He took a - way my sin, I know His love will leave me ne - ver. Re-con-ciled, I am His child, I know it was on me He smiled; I'm re-con-ciled, I'm

re-con-ciled to God,_____ hal-le-lu-jah! I'm

1 Reconciled, I'm reconciled,
  I'm reconciled to God for ever;
  know He took away my sin,
  I know His love will leave me never.
  Reconciled, I am His child,
  I know it was on me He smiled;
  I'm reconciled, I'm reconciled to God,
      hallelujah!

2 I'm justified, I'm justified,
  it's just as if I'd never sinned;
  and once I knew such guilty fear,
  but now I know His peace with me.
  Justified, I'm justified,
  it's all because my Jesus died;
  I'm justified, I'm justified by God,
      hallelujah!

3 I'll magnify, I'll magnify,
  I'll magnify His name for ever;
  wear the robe of righteousness
  and bless the name of Jesus, Saviour;
  magnify the One who died,
  the One who reigns for me on high;
  I'll magnify, I'll magnify my God.

569 Reach out and touch the Lord

Words and music: Bill Harmon

570   Reign in me

Words and music: Chris Bowater
Music arranged G Baker

Reign in me, sove-reign Lord, reign in me,
reign in me, sove-reign Lord,
reign in me. Cap-ti-vate my heart,
let Your king-dom come, es-tab-lish there Your
throne, let Your will be done!

Reigning in all splendour

Words and music: Dave Bilbrough
Music arranged Christopher Norton

Reign-ing in all splen - dour - vic-to-ri-ous love;

Christ Je-sus the Sav - iour,

tran-scen-dent a - bove. __ All earth-ly do-min-

-ions and king-doms shall fall, __

572   Rejoice!

Words and music: Graham Kendrick
Music arranged Christopher Norton

2 God is at work in us, His purpose to perform –
   building a kingdom of power not of words;
   where things impossible by faith shall be made possible:
   let's give the glory to Him now.
       Rejoice, rejoice . . .

3 Though we are weak, His grace is everything we need –
   we're made of clay, but this treasure is within;
   He turns our weaknesses into His opportunities,
   so that the glory goes to Him.
       Rejoice, rejoice . . .

573　Rejoice and be glad

REJOICE AND BE GLAD　Irregular

Words: Horatius Bonar (1808–89)
Music: John Jenkins Husband (1760–1825)

Re - joice and be glad! the Re - deem - er has come:
go,— look on His cra - dle, His cross, and His tomb.
Sound His prais - es, tell the sto - ry of Him who was slain;
sound His prais - es, tell with glad - ness He now lives a - gain.

1 Rejoice and be glad! the Redeemer has come:
go, look on His cradle, His cross, and His tomb.
Sound His praises, tell the story of Him who was slain;
sound His praises, tell with gladness He now lives again.

2 Rejoice and be glad! it is sunshine at last;
the clouds have departed, the shadows are past.
Sound His praises . . .

3 Rejoice and be glad! for the blood has been shed;
redemption is finished, the price has been paid.
Sound His praises . . .

4 Rejoice and be glad! now the pardon is free;
the just for the unjust has died on the tree.
Sound His praises . . .

5 Rejoice and be glad! for the Lamb that was slain,
o'er death is triumphant, and now lives again.
Sound His praises . . .

6 Rejoice and be glad! for our King is on high;
He pleads now for us on His throne in the sky.
Sound His praises . . .

7 Rejoice and be glad! for He's coming again;
He'll come in great glory, the Lamb that was slain.
Sound His praises . . .

574 Rejoice, rejoice, rejoice

Words and music: Chris Bowater

575   Rejoice, the Lord is King!

GOPSAL   66 66 88

Words: Charles Wesley (1707–88)
Music: G F Handel (1685–1759)

1 Rejoice, the Lord is King!
  your Lord and King adore;
  Mortals, give thanks and sing,
  and triumph evermore:
      Lift up your heart, lift up your voice;
      rejoice, again I say, rejoice.

2 Jesus the Saviour reigns,
  the God of truth and love;
  when He had purged our stains,
  He took His seat above:
      Lift up your heart . . .

3 His kingdom cannot fail,
  He rules o'er earth and heaven;
  the keys of death and hell
  are to our Jesus given:
      Lift up your heart . . .

4 He sits at God's right hand,
  till all His foes submit,
  and bow to His command,
  and fall beneath His feet:
      Lift up your heart . . .

5 Rejoice in glorious hope;
  Jesus the Judge shall come,
  and take His servants up
  to their eternal home:
      We soon shall hear the archangel's voice;
      the trump of God shall sound, rejoice!

576 Rejoice, the Lord is risen!

Words and music: Moira Austin

With strength and joy

Descant (3rd verse only)

Re - joice!

1 Re - joice,   the Lord is ris - en!
2 Re - joice,   the Lord is ris - en!
3 Re - joice,   the Lord is ris - en!

Re - joice!_____   wis - dom,   au -

__ He   is   the King of glo - ry;____ migh - ty Re -
__ We   are His ho - ly na - tion,____ ran - somed, for -
__ Bless - ing and hon - our give Him;____ wis - dom, au -

- tho - ri - ty,   be - long   to His   name:

- deem - er, He has   made us His own: re -
- giv - en,   washed in His pre - cious blood: re -
- tho - ri - ty, be - long to His name: re -

Chorus overleaf

577 Rejoice in the Lord always

Words: from Philippians 4
Music: Traditional
arranged Evelyn Tarner

A round in 4 parts

578 Revive Thy work, O Lord

SWABIA SM

Words: Albert Midlane (1825–1909)
Music: from a melody in J M Spiess'
Gesangbuch, 1745
arranged W H Havergal (1793–1870)

1 Revive Thy work, O Lord,
Thy mighty arm make bare;
speak with the voice that wakes the dead
and make Thy people hear.

2 Revive Thy work, O Lord,
disturb this sleep of death;
quicken the smouldering embers now
by Thine almighty breath.

3 Revive Thy work, O Lord,
create soul-thirst for Thee;
and hungering for the Bread of Life
O may our spirits be!

4 Revive Thy work, O Lord,
exalt Thy precious name;
and, by the Holy Ghost, our love
for Thee and Thine inflame.

5 Revive Thy work, O Lord,
give pentecostal showers;
the glory shall be all Thine own,
the blessing, Lord, be ours.

579   Restore, O Lord

Words and music: Graham Kendrick
and Chris Rolinson

Moderately fast

1 Re - store,   O Lord,   the hon - our of Your
2 Re - store,   O Lord,   in all the earth Your
3 Bend us,   O Lord,   where we are hard and

name!   In works of sove - reign pow — er come
fame,   and in our time re - vive   the
cold,   in Your re - fin - ers fire;   come

shake the earth a - gain,   that men may
Church that bears Your name,   and in Your
pu - ri - fy the gold: though suffer - ing

see,   and   come with rev – erent   fear   to   the
anger,   Lord, re – mem – ber   mer – cy,   O____
comes,   and   ev – il   crou – ches   near,   still our

Liv – ing   God,____   whose King – dom
Liv – ing   God,____   whose mer – cy
Liv – ing   God____   is   reign – ing,

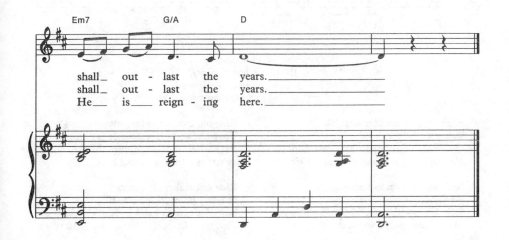

shall_ out – last   the   years.____
shall_ out – last   the   years.____
He__   is___ reign – ing   here.____

580   Ride on, ride on in majesty

ST DROSTANE   LM

Words: Henry Hart Milman (1791–1868)
Music: John Bacchus Dykes (1823–76)

1   Ride on, ride on in majesty!
    Hark, all the tribes hosanna cry,
    O Saviour meek, pursue Your road
    with palms and scattered garments strowed.

2   Ride on, ride on in majesty!
    in lowly pomp ride on to die:
    O Christ, Your triumphs now begin
    o'er captive death and conquered sin.

3   Ride on, ride on in majesty!
    The angel armies of the sky
    look down with sad and wondering eyes
    to see the approaching sacrifice.

4   Ride on, ride on in majesty!
    Your last and fiercest strife is nigh;
    the Father on His sapphire throne
    awaits His own anointed Son.

5   Ride on, ride on in majesty!
    in lowly pomp ride on to die;
    bow Your meek head to mortal pain,
    then take, O God, Your power, and reign.

581 River wash over me

Words and music: Dougie Brown
Music arranged David Peacock

Unhurried

1 River, wash over me,
   cleanse me and make me new;
   bathe me, refresh me and fill me anew –
   river, wash over me.

2 Spirit, watch over me,
   lead me to Jesus' feet;
   cause me to worship and fill me anew –
   Spirit, watch over me.

3 Jesus, rule over me,
   reign over all my heart;
   teach me to praise You and fill me anew –
   Jesus, rule over me.

582(i) Rock of ages

PETRA 77 77 77

Words: A M Toplady (1740–78)
Music: R Redhead (1820–1901)

Rock of a-ges, cleft for me, let me hide my-self in Thee;

let the wa-ter and the blood, from Thy riv-en side which flowed,

be of sin the dou-ble cure, cleanse me from its guilt and power.

1 Rock of ages, cleft for me,
   let me hide myself in Thee;
   let the water and the blood,
   from Thy riven side which flowed,
   be of sin the double cure,
   cleanse me from its guilt and power.

2 Not the labour of my hands
   can fulfil Thy law's demands;
   could my zeal no respite know,
   could my tears for ever flow,
   all for sin could not atone;
   Thou must save, and Thou alone.

3 Nothing in my hand I bring,
   simply to Thy cross I cling;
   naked, come to Thee for dress,
   helpless, look to Thee for grace;
   foul, I to the fountain fly;
   wash me, Saviour, or I die.

4 While I draw this fleeting breath,
   when mine eyes shall close in death,
   when I soar through tracts unknown,
   see Thee on Thy judgement throne;
   Rock of ages, cleft for me,
   let me hide myself in Thee.

582(ii)   Rock of ages

TOPLADY   77 77 77

Words and music: A M Toplady (1740–78)

Rock of a - ges, cleft for me, let me

hide my - self in Thee; let the wa - ter and the

blood, from Thy riv - en side which flowed, be of

sin the dou - ble cure, cleanse me from its guilt and power.

583   Safe in the shadow of the Lord

CREATOR GOD   CM

Words: Timothy Dudley-Smith
Music: Norman Warren

1 Safe in the shadow of the Lord
    beneath His hand and power,
      I trust in Him,
      I trust in Him,
    my fortress and my tower.

2 My hope is set on God alone
    though Satan spreads his snare,
      I trust in Him,
      I trust in Him
    to keep me in His care.

3 From fears and phantoms of the night,
    from foes about my way,
      I trust in Him,
      I trust in Him
    by darkness as by day.

4 His holy angels keep my feet
    secure from every stone;
      I trust in Him,
      I trust in Him,
    and unafraid go on.

5 Strong in the everlasting name,
    and in my Father's care,
      I trust in Him,
      I trust in Him
    who hears and answers prayer.

6 Safe in the shadow of the Lord,
    possessed by love divine,
      I trust in Him,
      I trust in Him,
    and meet His love with mine.

584 Saviour, again to Thy dear name

ELLERS   10 10 10 10

Words: John Ellerton (1826–93)
Music: E J Hopkins (1818–1901)
arranged Arthur Sullivan (1842–1900)

1 Saviour, again to Thy dear name we raise
   with one accord our parting hymn of praise;
   we stand to bless Thee ere our worship cease,
   then, lowly kneeling, wait Thy word of peace.

2 Grant us Thy peace upon our homeward way;
   with Thee began, with Thee shall end the day;
   guard Thou the lips from sin, the hearts from shame,
   that in this house have called upon Thy name.

3 Grant us Thy peace, Lord, through the coming night;
   turn Thou for us its darkness into light;
   from harm and danger keep Thy children free,
   for dark and light are both alike to Thee.

4 Grant us Thy peace throughout our earthly life,
   our balm in sorrow, and our stay in strife;
   then, when Thy voice shall bid our conflict cease,
   call us, O Lord, to Thine eternal peace.

585   Saviour of the world

Words and music: Greg Leavers
Music arranged Phil Burt

Begin slowly – with increasing
excitement in verses 2 and 3

Sav-iour of the world, thank You for dy-ing on the cross. All
praise to You our ris-en Lord, Hal-le-lu-jah! Je - sus.

In the gar-den of Geth-se-ma-ne Je-sus knelt and prayed;
for He knew the time was near when He would be be-trayed.

Saviour of the world,
thank You for dying on the cross.
All praise to You our risen Lord,
Hallelujah! Jesus.

1   In the garden of Gethsemane Jesus knelt and prayed;
    for He knew the time was near when He would be betrayed.
    God gave Him the strength to cope with all that people did to hurt Him;
    soldiers laughed and forced a crown of thorns upon His head.
        Saviour of the world . . .

2   On a cross outside the city they nailed Jesus high;
    innocent, but still He suffered as they watched Him die.
    Nothing that the soldiers did could make Him lose control, for Jesus
    knew the time to die, then 'It is finished', was His cry.
        Saviour of the world . . .

3   Three days later by God's power He rose up from the dead,
    for the tomb could not hold Jesus it was as He'd said;
    victor over sin and death, He conquered Satan's power; so let us
    celebrate that Jesus is alive for evermore.
        Saviour of the world . . .

586 Saviour, Thy dying love

PHELPS   64 64 66 64

Words: Sylvanus Dryden Phelps (1816–95)
Music: Robert Lowry (1826–99)

Sav - iour, Thy dy - ing love Thou gav - est me,
nor should I aught with-hold, my Lord, from Thee;
in love my soul would bow, my heart ful - fil its vow,
some off - ering bring Thee now, some - thing for Thee.

1 Saviour, Thy dying love
      Thou gavest me,
   nor should I aught withhold,
      my Lord, from Thee;
   in love my soul would bow,
   my heart fulfil its vow,
   some offering bring Thee now,
      something for Thee.

2 At the blest mercy-seat
      pleading for me,
   my feeble faith looks up,
      Jesus, to Thee:
   help me the cross to bear,
   Thy wondrous love declare,
   some song to raise, or prayer –
      something for Thee.

3 Give me a faithful heart,
      likeness to Thee,
   that each departing day
      henceforth may see
   some work of love begun,
   some deed of kindness done,
   some wanderer sought and won –
      something for Thee.

4 All that I am and have,
      Thy gifts so free,
   in joy, in grief, through life,
      O Lord, for Thee.
   And when Thy face I see,
   my ransomed soul shall be,
   through all eternity,
      something for Thee.

587   Search me, O God

Words: J Edwin Orr
arranged from an old Maori melody

Search me, O God, and know my heart to-day; try me, O Lord, and know my thoughts I pray: see if there be some wick-ed way in me,

Music: Reproduced by permission
of EMI Music Publishing Ltd

cleanse   me   from   ev - ery sin   and   set   me   free._____

1   Search me, O God, and know my heart today;
    try me, O Lord, and know my thoughts I pray:
    see if there be some wicked way in me,
    cleanse me from every sin and set me free.

2   I praise Thee, Lord, for cleansing me from sin;
    fulfil Thy word, and make me pure within;
    fill me with fire, where once I burned with shame,
    grant my desire to magnify Thy name.

3   Lord, take my life, and make it wholly Thine;
    fill my poor heart with Thy great love divine;
    take all my will, my passion, self and pride;
    I now surrender – Lord, in me abide.

4   O Holy Ghost, revival comes from Thee;
    send a revival – start the work in me:
    Thy word declares Thou wilt supply our need;
    for blessing now, O Lord, I humbly plead.

588   See, amid the winter's snow

HUMILITY   77 77 with refrain

Words: Edward Caswall (1814–78)
Music: John Goss (1800–80)

1 See, amid the winter's snow,
born for us on earth below,
see, the Lamb of God appears,
promised from eternal years.
   Hail, thou ever-blessèd morn!
   Hail, redemption's happy dawn!
   Sing through all Jerusalem,
   Christ is born in Bethlehem!

2 Lo, within a manger lies
He who built the starry skies,
He who, throned in height sublime,
sits amid the cherubim.
   Hail, thou ever-blessèd morn . . .

3 Say, ye holy shepherds, say,
what your joyful news today;
wherefore have ye left your sheep
on the lonely mountain steep?
   Hail, thou ever-blessèd morn . . .

4 As we watched at dead of night,
Lo, we saw a wondrous light:
angels singing, 'Peace on earth'
told us of the Saviour's birth.
   Hail, thou ever-blessèd morn . . .

5 Sacred infant, all divine,
what a tender love was Thine,
thus to come from highest bliss
down to such a world as this!
   Hail, thou ever-blessèd morn . . .

6 Teach, O teach us, holy child,
by Thy face so meek and mild,
teach us to resemble Thee
in Thy sweet humility.
   Hail, thou ever-blessèd morn . . .

589 See Him lying on a bed of straw

CALYPSO CAROL   Irregular

Words and music: Michael Perry
Music arranged Stephen Coates

See Him ly - ing on a bed of straw: _ a draugh-ty sta - ble with an o - pen door; Ma - ry cra - dl-ing the babe she bore — the Prince of glo - ry is His name.

O now car - ry me to Beth - le - hem __ to

see the Lord_ ap-pear to men — just as poor_ as was the sta-ble then, the Prince of glo-ry when He came.

1 See Him lying on a bed of straw:
   a draughty stable with an open door;
   Mary cradling the babe she bore –
   the Prince of glory is His name.
       O now carry me to Bethlehem
       to see the Lord appear to men –
       just as poor as was the stable then,
       the Prince of glory when He came.

2 Star of silver, sweep across the skies,
   show where Jesus in the manger lies;
   shepherds, swiftly from your stupor rise
   to see the Saviour of the world!
       O now carry . . .

3 Angels, sing the song that you began,
   bring God's glory to the heart of man;
   sing that Bethl'em's little baby can
   be salvation to the soul.
       O now carry . . .

4 Mine are riches, from Your poverty,
   from Your innocence, eternity;
   mine forgiveness by Your death for me,
   child of sorrow for my joy.
       O now carry . . .

590 Seek ye first

Words and music: Karen Lafferty
Music arranged Roland Fudge

Rich and broad

Seek ye first the kingdom of God, and His righteousness, and all these things shall be added unto you. Allelu, allelu ia. Alleluia, alle Seek ye first the kingdom of God, and His righteous

1 Seek ye first the kingdom of God,
   and His righteousness,
   and all these things shall be added unto you.
   Allelu, alleluia.
   Seek ye first . . .

2 Man shall not live by bread alone,
   but by every word
   that proceeds from the mouth of God.
   Allelu, alleluia.
   Man shall not . . .

3 Ask and it shall be given unto you,
   seek and ye shall find;
   knock and the door shall be opened up to you.
   Allelu, alleluia.
   Ask and it shall . . .

591

Seek ye the Lord

Words and music: Joan Parsons
Music arranged Roland Fudge

1 Seek ye the Lord all ye peo - ple,_____ turn to Him
2 Ho ev - ery - one who is thir - sty,_____ come to the

while He is near;_____ let the wick-ed for - sake his own
wa - ters of life;_____ come and drink of the milk and the

way, and call on Him while He may hear._____ come with-out
wine,__

mo - ney and price. And there is peace like a
love ev - er

ri - ver,_____ and glo - ry di - vine, if you'll
flow-ing,_____ and joy ev - er full; and there's

come to the wa - ter, if you'll taste of His
life ev - er - last-ing

wine. There is for us all._____

1 Seek ye the Lord all ye people,
   turn to Him while He is near;
   let the wicked forsake his own way,
   and call on Him while He may hear.

2 Ho everyone who is thirsty,
   come to the waters of life;
   come and drink of the milk and the wine,
   come without money and price.

   And there is peace like a river,
   and glory divine,
   if you'll come to the water,
   if you'll taste of His wine.
   There is love ever flowing,
   and joy ever full;
   and there's life everlasting
   for us all.

592   See Him on the cross

Words and music: Ruth Hooke

1 See Him on the cross of shame dy - ing for
(2) laid Him in a gar - den tomb, and sealed it with a

me, bear - ing all my guilt and pain,
stone. Ma - ry wept her tears of grief - her

dy - ing for me.
pre - cious Lord had gone:

Chorus overleaf

Triumphantly

Je - sus lives, Je - sus lives,

Je - sus lives in___ me:_____ I will praise Your name.   2 They

1   See Him on the cross of shame
    dying for me,
    bearing all my guilt and pain,
    dying for me.
    And how I love You,
    Jesus my Redeemer;
    You gave Your life for me, O Lord,
    now I give my life to You.
      Jesus lives, Jesus lives,
      Jesus lives in me:
      I will praise Your name.

2   They laid Him in a garden tomb,
    and sealed it with a stone.
    Mary wept her tears of grief –
    her precious Lord had gone:
    'And how I love You,
    Jesus my Redeemer';
    then she looked – the stone was rolled away –
    He had triumphed over death.
      Jesus lives . . .

593   Send forth the gospel

OMBERSLEY   LM

Words: H E Fox (1841–1926)
Music: W H Gladstone (1840–91)

1 Send forth the gospel! Let it run
  southward and northward, east and west:
  tell all the earth Christ died and lives,
  He offers pardon, life, and rest.

2 Send forth Your gospel, mighty Lord!
  Out of the chaos bring to birth
  Your own creation's promised hope;
  the better days of heaven on earth.

3 Send forth Your gospel, gracious Lord!
  Yours was the blood for sinners shed;
  Your voice still pleads in human hearts;
  to You may all Your sheep be led.

4 Send forth Your gospel, holy Lord!
  Kindle in us love's sacred flame;
  love giving all and grudging naught
  for Jesus' sake, in Jesus' name.

5 Send forth the gospel! Tell it out!
  Go, brothers, at the Master's call;
  prepare His way, who comes to reign
  the King of kings and Lord of all.

594 Send me out from here

Words and music: John Pantry
Music arranged Christopher Norton

Majestically

Send me out from here Lord, to serve a world in
need; may I know no man by the coat he wears, but the
heart that Je-sus sees. And may the light of Your face
shine up-on me Lord – You have filled my heart with the

Words and music: © Ears and Eyes Music Ltd/Boosey & Hawkes Music Publishers Ltd,
295 Regent Street, London W1R 8JH

595

Set my spirit free

Words and music: Unknown
Music arranged Phil Burt

Set my spi-rit free that I might wor - ship You;

set my spi-rit free that I might praise Your name.

Let all bond-age go and let de - liv - erance flow;

set my spi-rit free to wor-ship You._____

596 Show Your power, O Lord

Words and music: Graham Kendrick
Music arranged Christopher Norton

1 Show Your power, O Lord,_ de-mon-strate the just-ice of Your king-dom; prove Your migh-ty word,_ vin-di-cate Your name be-fore a watch-ing world._____

2 Show Your power, O Lord,_ cause Your church to rise_ and take_ ac-tion; let all fear be gone;_ pow-ers of the age_ to come are break-ing through._____

597   Silent night

STILLE NACHT   Irregular

Words: Joseph Mohr (1792–1848)
tr. S A Brooke (1832–1916)
Music: Franz Gruber (1787–1863)

1   Silent night, holy night!
    Sleeps the world; hid from sight,
    Mary and Joseph in stable bare
    watched o'er the child belovèd and fair
      sleeping in heavenly rest,
      sleeping in heavenly rest.

2   Silent night, holy night!
    Shepherds first saw the light,
    heard resounding clear and long,
    far and near, the angel-song:
      'Christ the Redeemer is here,
      Christ the Redeemer is here.'

3   Silent night, holy night!
    Son of God, O how bright
    love is smiling from Your face!
    Strikes for us now the hour of grace,
      Saviour, since You are born,
      Saviour, since You are born.

598

Silver and gold

Words and music: Anon
Music arranged Betty Pulkingham

Peter and John went to pray, they met a lame man on the way; he
'Silver and gold have I none, but such as I have give I thee. In the

asked for alms and held out his palms, and this is what Peter did
name of Jesus Christ of Nazareth, rise up and

1.
say: walk!'
2.
He went walking and leaping and

praising God, walking and leaping and praising God. 'In the

name of Jesus Christ of Nazareth, rise up and walk!'

599   Sing a new song to the Lord

ONSLOW SQUARE   7 7 11 8

Words: Timothy Dudley-Smith
Music: David Wilson

1 Sing a new song to the Lord, He to whom won-ders be-
2 Now to the ends of the earth, see His sal - va-tion is
3 Sing a new song and re - joice, pub - lish His prais-es a-
4 Join with the hills and the sea, thun-ders of praise to pro-

- long:_____ re - joice_____ in His tri - umph__ and
shown:_____ and still_____ He re - mem - bers__ His
- broad:_____ let voi - ces_____ in__ cho - rus,__ with
- long:_____ in judge-ment__ and__ jus - tice__ He

tell_____ of His power,_____ O sing_____ to the
mer - cy____ and__ truth,_____ un - chang - ing in
trum - pet__ and__ horn,_____ re - sound__ for the
comes_____ to the earth,_____ O sing_____ to the

1-3.

4.

Lord_____ a new song!
love_____ to His own.
joy_____ of the Lord!
Lord_____ a new song!

600   Sing to God new songs of worship

ODE TO JOY   87 87 D

Words: from Psalm 98
Michael Baughen
Music: L van Beethoven (1770–1827)

1 Sing to God new songs of wor-ship – all His deeds are mar-vel-lous;
2 Sing to God new songs of wor-ship – earth has seen His vic-to-ry;
3 Sing to God new songs of wor-ship – let the sea now make a noise;

He has brought sal-va-tion to us with His hand and ho-ly arm:
let the lands of earth be joy-ful prais-ing Him with thank-ful-ness:
all on earth and in the wa-ters sound your prais-es to the Lord:

He has shown to all the_ na-tions right-eous-ness and sav-ing power;
sound up-on the harp His prais-es, play to_ Him with me-lo-dy;_
let the hills be joy-ful to-geth-er, let the_ ri-vers clap their hands,

He re-called His truth and mer-cy to His peo-ple Is-ra-el.
let the trum-pets sound His_ tri-umph, show your joy to God the king!
for with right-eous-ness and_ jus-tice He will come to judge the earth.

601   Sing alleluia to the Lord

Words and music: Linda Stassen
Music arranged Norman Warren

1. Sing alleluia to the Lord,
   sing alleluia to the Lord,
   sing alleluia, sing alleluia,
   sing alleluia to the Lord!

2. Jesus is risen from the dead,
   Jesus is risen from the dead,
   Jesus is risen, Jesus is risen,
   Jesus is risen from the dead!

3. Jesus is Lord of heaven and earth,
   Jesus is Lord of heaven and earth,
   Jesus is Lord, Jesus is Lord,
   Jesus is Lord of heaven and earth.

4. Jesus is coming for His own,
   Jesus is coming for His own,
   Jesus is coming, Jesus is coming,
   Jesus is coming for His own.

602

Sing we the King

THE GLORY SONG   10 10 10 10 with refrain

Words: C Silvester Horne (1865–1914)
Music: C H Gabriel (1856–1932)

Sing we the King who is com-ing to reign, glo-ry to Je-sus, the

Lamb that was slain; life and sal - va-tion His em-pire shall bring,

joy to the na-tions when Je - sus is King.___ *Come let us*
Come___
Come let us

sing: *praise to our King.*   *Je - sus our King,*
— let us   sing: *praise to our   King.*   *Je - sus our*
sing: praise to our   King.___   Je - sus our   King,___

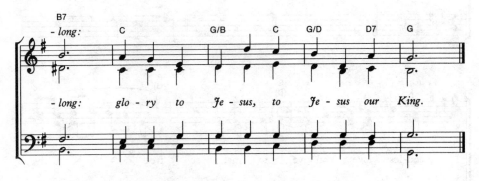

1 Sing we the King who is coming to reign,
glory to Jesus, the Lamb that was slain;
life and salvation His empire shall bring,
joy to the nations when Jesus is King.
Come let us sing: praise to our King.
Jesus our King, Jesus our King:
this is our song, who to Jesus belong:
glory to Jesus, to Jesus our King.

2 All men shall dwell in His marvellous light,
races long severed His love shall unite;
justice and truth from His sceptre shall spring,
wrong shall be ended when Jesus is King.
Come let us sing . . .

3 All shall be well in His kingdom of peace,
freedom shall flourish and wisdom increase;
foe shall be friend when His triumph we sing,
sword shall be sickle when Jesus is King.
Come let us sing . . .

4 Souls shall be saved from the burden of sin;
doubt shall not darken his witness within;
hell hath no terrors, and death hath no sting;
love is victorious, when Jesus is King.
Come let us sing . . .

5 Kingdom of Christ, for Thy coming we pray,
hasten, O Father, the dawn of the day;
when this new song Thy creation shall sing,
Satan is vanquished and Jesus is King.
Come let us sing . . .

603   So freely

Words and music: Dave Bilbrough
Music arranged David Peacock

Flowing, with a sense of mystery

So free - ly___ flows the
end-less love You give___ to me; so free - ly,___
___ not de - pen-dent on___ my part.___ As I am
reach-ing out,_ re-veal the love with-in Your heart;___

as I am reach-ing out,_ re-veal the love with-in Your

heart._____ 2 Com -

1 So freely
   flows the endless love You give to me;
   so freely,
   not dependent on my part.
   As I am reaching out,
   reveal the love within Your heart;
   as I am reaching out,
   reveal the love within Your heart.

2 Completely –
   that's the way You give Your love to me,
   completely,
   not dependent on my part.
   As I am reaching out,
   reveal the love within Your heart,
   as I am reaching out,
   reveal the love within Your heart.

3 So easy,
   I receive the love You give to me;
   so easy,
   not dependent on my part.
   Flowing out to me –
   the love within Your heart;
   flowing out to me –
   the love within Your heart.

604 Soldiers of Christ, arise

FROM STRENGTH TO STRENGTH   DSM

Words: Charles Wesley (1707–88)
Music: Edward Woodall Naylor (1867–1934)

Sol - diers of Christ, a - rise, and put your ar - mour on, strong in the strength which God sup - plies through His e - ter - nal Son. Strong in the Lord of hosts, and in His migh - ty power; who in the

strength of Je - sus trusts is more than con - que - ror.

1 Soldiers of Christ, arise,
  and put your armour on,
  strong in the strength which God supplies
  through His eternal Son.
  Strong in the Lord of hosts,
  and in His mighty power;
  who in the strength of Jesus trusts
  is more than conqueror.

2 Stand then in His great might,
  with all His strength endued;
  and take, to arm you for the fight,
  the panoply of God:
  to keep your armour bright,
  attend with constant care,
  still walking in your Captain's sight
  and watching unto prayer.

3 From strength to strength go on,
  wrestle and fight and pray;
  tread all the powers of darkness down
  and win the well-fought day.
  That, having all things done,
  and all your conflicts past,
  ye may o'ercome through Christ alone,
  and stand entire at last.

605

Soon, and very soon

Words and music: Andraé Crouch

Soon, and ve-ry soon,__ we are go-ing to see the King;__

soon, and ve-ry soon,__ we are go-ing to see the King;__

soon, and ve-ry soon,__ we are go-ing to see the King;

__ al-le - lu - ia,__ al-le - lu - ia,__ we're going to see the King!

1 Soon, and very soon,
we are going to see the King;
soon, and very soon,
we are going to see the King;
soon, and very soon,
we are going to see the King;
alleluia, alleluia,
we're going to see the King!

2 No more crying there . . .
alleluia . . .

3 No more dying there . . .
alleluia . . .
Alleluia, alleluia, alleluia, alleluia.

4 Soon and very soon . . .
alleluia . . .
Alleluia, alleluia, alleluia, alleluia.

606 Soften my heart

Words and music: Graham Kendrick
Music arranged Christopher Norton

607   Souls of men, why will ye scatter

CROSS OF JESUS   87 87

Words: Frederick William Faber (1814–63)
Music: John Stainer (1840–1901)

1   Souls of men, why will ye scatter
like a crowd of frightened sheep?
Foolish hearts, why will ye wander
from a love so true and deep?

2   Was there ever kindest shepherd
half so gentle, half so sweet,
as the Saviour who would have us
come and gather round His feet?

3   There's a wideness in God's mercy,
like the wideness of the sea;
there's a kindness in His justice,
which is more than liberty.

4   There is plentiful redemption
in the blood that has been shed;
there is joy for all the members
in the sorrows of the Head.

5   For the love of God is broader
than the measures of man's mind;
and the heart of the Eternal
is most wonderfully kind.

6   If our love were but more simple,
we should take Him at His word,
and our lives would be all sunshine
in the sweetness of our Lord.

608   Speak, Lord, in the stillness

QUIETUDE   65 65

Words: Emily Mary Crawford (1864–1927)
Music: Harold Green (1871–1931)

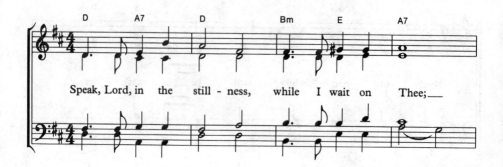

Speak, Lord, in the still - ness, while I wait on Thee; ___

hushed my heart to lis - ten in ex-pec - tan - cy.

1 Speak, Lord, in the stillness,
   while I wait on Thee;
   hushed my heart to listen
   in expectancy.

2 Speak, O blessèd Master,
   in this quiet hour;
   let me see Thy face, Lord,
   feel Thy touch of power.

3 For the words Thou speakest,
   they are life indeed;
   living Bread from heaven,
   now my spirit feed!

4 All to Thee is yielded,
   I am not my own;
   blissful, glad surrender –
   I am Thine alone.

5 Speak, Thy servant heareth!
   be not silent, Lord;
   waits my soul upon Thee
   for the quickening word!

6 Fill me with the knowledge
   of Thy glorious will;
   all Thine own good pleasure
   in Thy child fulfil.

609   Spirit of God

Words and music: Chris Bowater

Spi - rit of God, show me Je-sus;
re - move the dark - ness, let truth shine through.
Spi - rit of God, show me Je-sus;
re - veal the ful - ness of His love to me!

610

Spirit of God divine

Words and music: Colin Preston
Music arranged Chris Mitchell

Spi - rit of God di - vine,_____ fill this heart of_ mine_____ with ho - ly flame, to praise the name of Je - sus my Lord._____ *Fill me a - gain,*_____

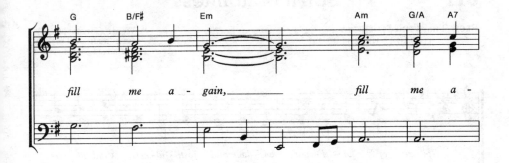

fill me a - gain,_____ fill me a -

- gain,_____ O Spi - rit of the Lord._____

1 Spirit of God divine,
  fill this heart of mine
  with holy flame,
  to praise the name
  of Jesus my Lord.
    Fill me again,
    fill me again,
    fill me again,
    O Spirit of the Lord.

2 Spirit of God divine,
  fill this mouth of mine
  with holy praise,
  to set the earth ablaze
  and glorify Your name.
    Fill me again . . .

3 Spirit of God divine,
  take this heart of mine
  to Your throne this day;
  help me, I pray,
  my offering to give.
    Fill me again . . .

611

Spirit of holiness

BLOW THE WIND SOUTHERLY
12 10 12 10 12 11 12 11

Words: Christopher Idle
Music: traditional melody
arranged John Barnard

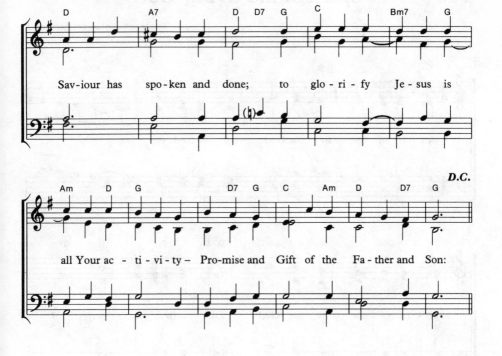

Sav-iour has spo-ken and done; to glo-ri-fy Je-sus is

all Your ac-ti-vi-ty — Pro-mise and Gift of the Fa-ther and Son:

D.C.

Spirit of holiness,
wisdom and faithfulness,
Wind of the Lord,
blowing strongly and free:
strength of our serving
and joy of our worshipping –
Spirit of God,
bring Your fulness to me!

1 You came to interpret and teach us effectively
all that the Saviour has spoken and done;
to glorify Jesus is all Your activity –
Promise and Gift of the Father and Son:
Spirit of holiness . . .

2 You came with Your gifts to supply all our poverty,
pouring Your love on the church in her need;
You came with Your fruit for our growth to maturity,
richly refreshing the souls that You feed:
Spirit of holiness . . .

612 Spirit of the living God

Words and music: Paul Armstrong

Spi - rit of the liv - ing God fall a-fresh on me;

Spi - rit of the liv - ing God fall a-fresh on me;

fill me a - new, fill me a - new;

Spi - rit of the Lord fall a - fresh on me.

613 Spirit of the living God

Words and music: Daniel Iverson
Music arranged W G Hathaway

Spi - rit of the liv - ing God, fall a-fresh on me;

Spi - rit of the liv - ing God, fall a-fresh on me;

break me, melt me, mould me, fill me;

Spi - rit of the liv - ing God, fall a-fresh on me.

614   Spirit divine

EMMAUS   CM

Words: Andrew Reed (1787–1862)
Music: Unknown

1   Spirit divine, attend our prayers,
    and make this house Thy home;
    descend with all Thy gracious powers,
    O come, great Spirit, come!

2   Come as the light; to us reveal
    our emptiness and woe;
    and lead us in those paths of life
    where all the righteous go.

3   Come as the fire; and purge our hearts
    like sacrificial flame;
    let our whole soul an offering be
    to our Redeemer's name.

4   Come as the Dove; and spread Thy wings,
    the wings of perfect love;
    and let Thy Church on earth become
    blest as the Church above.

5   Spirit divine, attend our prayers,
    make a lost world Thy home;
    descend with all Thy gracious powers,
    O come, great Spirit, come!

615   Stand up and bless the Lord

St Michael   SM

Words: James Montgomery (1771–1854)
Music: from the *Genevan Psalter*, 1551

Stand up and bless the Lord, ye peo-ple of His choice;

stand up and bless the Lord your God, with heart and soul and voice.

1   Stand up and bless the Lord,
    ye people of His choice;
    stand up and bless the Lord your God,
    with heart and soul and voice.

2   Though high above all praise,
    above all blessing high;
    who would not fear His holy name?
    and laud and magnify?

3   O for the living flame
    from His own altar brought,
    O touch our lips, our minds inspire,
    and wing to heaven our thought!

4   There, with benign regard,
    our hymns He deigns to hear;
    though unrevealed to mortal sense,
    our spirits feel Him near.

5   God is our strength and song,
    and His salvation ours;
    then be His love in Christ proclaimed
    with all our ransomed powers.

6   Stand up and bless the Lord,
    the Lord your God adore;
    stand up and bless His glorious name
    henceforth for evermore.

616 Stand up and bless the Lord

Words and music: Andy Silver

617   Stand up! stand up for Jesus

MORNING LIGHT   76 76 D

Words: George Duffield (1818–88)
Music: G J Webb (1803–87)

Stand up! stand up for Je-sus! ye sol-diers of the cross,

lift high His roy-al ban-ner; it must not suf-fer loss.

From vic-tory un-to vic-tory His_ ar-my shall He lead,___

till ev-ery foe is van-quished and Christ is Lord in-deed.

1   Stand up! stand up for Jesus!
    ye soldiers of the cross,
    lift high His royal banner;
    it must not suffer loss.
    From victory unto victory
    His army shall He lead,
    till every foe is vanquished
    and Christ is Lord indeed.

2   Stand up! stand up for Jesus!
    the trumpet-call obey;
    forth to the mighty conflict
    in this His glorious day.
    Ye that are men, now serve Him
    against unnumbered foes;
    let courage rise with danger,
    and strength to strength oppose.

3   Stand up! stand up for Jesus!
    stand in His strength alone;
    the arm of flesh will fail you,
    ye dare not trust your own.
    Put on the gospel armour,
    each piece put on with prayer;
    where duty calls, or danger,
    be never wanting there.

4   Stand up! stand up for Jesus!
    the strife will not be long;
    the day the noise of battle,
    the next the victor's song.
    To him that overcometh
    a crown of life shall be;
    he with the King of glory
    shall reign eternally.

618

Sun of my soul

ABENDS   LM

Words: John Keble (1792–1866)
Music: Herbert Stanley Oakley (1830–1903)

Sun of my soul, my Sav - iour dear,
it is not night if You are near;
O may no earth - born cloud a - rise
to hide You from Your ser - vant's eyes.

1 Sun of my soul, my Saviour dear,
it is not night if You are near;
O may no earth-born cloud arise
to hide You from Your servant's eyes.

2 When the soft dews of kindly sleep
my wearied eyelids gently steep,
be my last thought, how sweet to rest
for ever on my Saviour's breast!

3 Abide with me from morn till eve,
for without You I cannot live;
abide with me when night is nigh,
for without You I dare not die.

4 If some poor wandering child of Yours
have spurned today Your holy voice,
now, Lord, the gracious work begin;
let them no more be ruled by sin.

5 Watch by the sick; enrich the poor
with blessings from Your boundless store;
be every mourner's sleep tonight,
like infant's slumbers, pure and light.

6 Come near and bless us when we wake,
ere through the world our way we take;
till in the ocean of Your love
we lose ourselves in heaven above.

619   Such love

Words and music: Graham Kendrick
Music arranged Christopher Norton

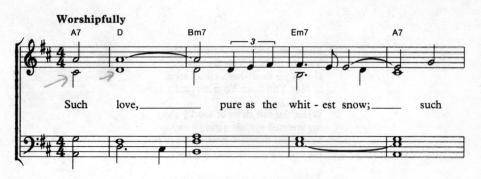

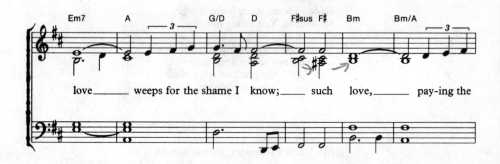

1 Such love, pure as the whitest snow;
  such love weeps for the shame I know;
  such love, paying the debt I owe;
  O Jesus, such love.

2 Such love, stilling my restlessness;
  such love, filling my emptiness;
  such love, showing me holiness;
  O Jesus, such love.

3 Such love springs from eternity;
  such love, streaming through history;
  such love, fountain of life to me;
  O Jesus, such love.

620 Sweet is the work

DEEP HARMONY LM

Words: Isaac Watts (1674–1748)
Music: Handel Parker (1857–1928)

1 Sweet is the work, my God, my King,
  to praise Thy name, give thanks and sing,
  to show Thy love by morning light,
  and talk of all Thy truth at night.

2 Sweet is the day of sacred rest,
  no mortal cares disturb my breast;
  O may my heart in tune be found,
  like David's harp of solemn sound.

3 My heart shall triumph in the Lord,
  and bless His works, and bless His word;
  Thy works of grace, how bright they shine,
  how deep Thy counsels, how divine!

4 And I shall share a glorious part,
  when grace has well refined my heart,
  and fresh supplies of joy are shed,
  like holy oil, to cheer my head.

5 Then shall I see and hear and know
  all I desired or wished below;
  and every power find sweet employ
  in that eternal world of joy.

621 Swing wide the gates

Words and music: Chris Bowater

Swing wide the gates,
let the King come in.
Swing wide the gates,
make a way for Him.
Here He comes,

622 Take, eat, this is My body

Words and music: Paul Simmons
Music arranged Christopher Norton

623　Take heart and praise our God

CHRISTCHURCH　66 66 88

Words: David Mowbray
Music: C Steggall (1826–1905)

1　Take heart and praise our God;
　　rejoice and clap your hands –
　　His power our foe subdued,
　　His mercy ever stands:
　　　Let trumpets sound and people sing,
　　　The Lord through all the earth is King!

2　Take heart, but sing with fear,
　　exalt His worthy name;
　　with mind alert and clear
　　now celebrate His fame:
　　　Let trumpets sound . . .

3　Take heart for future days,
　　for tasks as yet unknown –
　　the God whose name we praise
　　is seated on the throne:
　　　Let trumpets sound . . .

4　Take heart and trust in God
　　the Father and the Son –
　　God is our strength and shield,
　　His Spirit guides us on:
　　　Let trumpets sound . . .

624 Take my life

NOTTINGHAM   77 77

Words: Frances Ridley Havergal (1836–79)
Music: Wolfgang Amadeus Mozart (1756–91)

1 Take my life, and let it be
consecrated, Lord, to Thee;
take my moments and my days,
let them flow in ceaseless praise.

2 Take my hands, and let them move
at the impulse of Thy love;
take my feet, and let them be
swift and beautiful for Thee.

3 Take my voice, and let me sing
always, only, for my King;
take my lips, and let them be
filled with messages from Thee.

4 Take my silver and my gold,
not a mite would I withhold;
take my intellect, and use
every power as Thou shalt choose.

5 Take my will, and make it Thine;
it shall be no longer mine:
take my heart, it is Thine own;
it shall be Thy royal throne.

6 Take my love; my Lord, I pour
at Thy feet its treasure store:
take myself, and I will be
ever, only, all, for Thee.

625   Take time to be holy

TAKE TIME TO BE HOLY   11 11 11 11

Words: W D Longstaff (1822–94)
Music: G C Stebbins (1846–1945)

Take time to be ho - ly, speak oft with Thy Lord;
a - bide in Him al - ways, and feed on His Word.
Make friends of God's child - ren, help those who are weak;
for - get-ting in no - thing His bless-ing to seek.

1 Take time to be holy, speak oft with Thy Lord;
abide in Him always, and feed on His word.
Make friends of God's children, help those who are weak;
forgetting in nothing His blessing to seek.

2 Take time to be holy, the world rushes on;
spend much time in secret with Jesus alone –
by looking to Jesus, like Him thou shalt be!
Thy friends in thy conduct His likeness shall see.

3 Take time to be holy, let Him be thy guide;
and run not before Him, whatever betide;
in joy or in sorrow still follow thy Lord,
and, looking to Jesus, still trust in His word.

4 Take time to be holy, be calm in thy soul;
each thought and each temper beneath His control;
thus led by His Spirit to fountains of love,
thou soon shalt be fitted for service above.

626   Teach me Thy way

THE PATH DIVINE   64 64 66 64   Words and music: B Mansell Ramsey (1849–1923)

1   Teach me Thy way, O Lord,
     teach me Thy way!
     Thy gracious aid afford,
     teach me Thy way!
     Help me to walk aright,
     more by faith, less by sight;
     lead me with heavenly light:
     teach me Thy way!

2   When doubts and fears arise,
     teach me Thy way!
     When storms o'erspread the skies,
     teach me Thy way!
     Shine through the cloud and rain,
     through sorrow, toil, and pain;
     make Thou my pathway plain:
     teach me Thy way!

3   Long as my life shall last,
     teach me Thy way!
     Where'er my lot be cast,
     teach me Thy way!
     Until the race is run,
     until the journey's done,
     until the crown is won,
     teach me Thy way!

627   Teach me to live

Words and music: Elizabeth M Dyke

Teach me to live, day by day, in Your

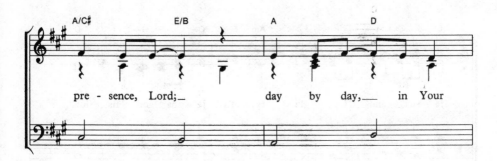

pre-sence, Lord; day by day, in Your

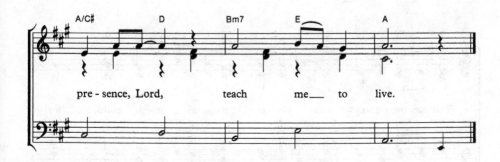

pre-sence, Lord, teach me to live.

1 Teach me to live, day by day,
   in Your presence, Lord;
   day by day, in Your presence, Lord,
   teach me to live.

2 Teach me to praise, day by day,
   in Your Spirit, Lord;
   day by day, in Your Spirit, Lord,
   teach me to praise.

3 Teach me to love, day by day,
   in Your power, Lord;
   day by day, in Your power, Lord,
   teach me to love.

4 Teach me to give, day by day,
   from my wealth, O Lord;
   day by day, from my wealth, O Lord,
   teach me to give.

628   Tell me the old, old story

TELL ME   76 76 D with refrain

Words: Arabella C Hankey (1834–1911) altd.
Music: W H Doane (1832–1916)

Tell me the old, old sto - ry of un - seen things a - bove,— of

Je - sus— and— His— glo - ry, of Je - sus— and His— love.

Tell me the sto - ry sim - ply, as to— a— lit - tle child, for

I am— weak and— wea - ry, and help - less— and de - filed.

Tell me the old, old sto - ry, tell me the old, old sto - ry,

tell me the old, old sto - ry of Je - sus and His love.

1 Tell me the old, old story
   of unseen things above,
   of Jesus and His glory,
   of Jesus and His love.
   Tell me the story simply,
   as to a little child,
   for I am weak and weary,
   and helpless and defiled.
       Tell me the old, old story,
       tell me the old, old story,
       tell me the old, old story
       of Jesus and His love.

2 Tell me the story slowly,
   that I may take it in –
   that wonderful redemption,
   God's remedy for sin.
   Tell me the story often,
   for I forget so soon:
   the early dew of morning
   has passed away at noon.
       Tell me the old . . .

3 Tell me the story softly,
   with earnest tones and grave;
   Remember! I'm the sinner
   whom Jesus came to save.
   Tell me the story always,
   if you would really be,
   in any time of trouble,
   a comforter to me.
       Tell me the old . . .

4 Tell me the same old story,
   when you have cause to fear
   that this world's empty glory
   is costing me too dear.
   Yes, and when that world's glory
   is dawning on my soul,
   tell me the old, old story;
   'Christ Jesus makes you whole.'
       Tell me the old . . .

629 Tell me the stories of Jesus

STORIES OF JESUS 84 84 54 54

Words: W H Parker (1845–1929) altd.
verse 6 by Hugh Martin (1890–1964)
altered Horrobin/Leavers
Music: F A Challinor (1866–1952)

1 Tell me the stories of Jesus
  I love to hear;
  things I would ask Him to tell me
  if He were here;
  scenes by the wayside,
  tales of the sea,
  stories of Jesus,
  tell them to me.

2 First let me hear how the children
  stood round His knee;
  that I may know of His blessing
  resting on me;
  words full of kindness,
  deeds full of grace,
  signs of the love found
  in Jesus' face.

3 Tell me, in words full of wonder,
  how rolled the sea,
  tossing the boat in a tempest
  on Galilee.
  Jesus then doing
  His Father's will,
  ended the storm saying
  'Peace, peace, be still.'

4 Into the city I'd follow
  the children's band,
  waving a branch of the palm-tree
  high in my hand;
  worshipping Jesus,
  yes, I would sing
  loudest hosannas,
  for He is King!

5 Show me that scene in the garden,
  of bitter pain;
  and of the cross where my Saviour
  for me was slain;
  and, through the sadness,
  help me to see
  how Jesus suffered
  for love of me.

6 Gladly I'd hear of His rising
  out of the grave,
  living and strong and triumphant,
  mighty to save:
  and how He sends us
  all men to bring
  stories of Jesus,
  Jesus, their King.

630 Tell My people

Words (chorus) and music: Leonard Bartlotti
verses and descant Jan Harrington

Tell My peo-ple I love____ them,____ tell My peo-ple I care;____ when they feel far a-way from Me,____ tell My peo-ple I am there.

Tell My peo-ple I came and died____ to give them lib-er-ty;____

Verses and music arrangement: © 1975 Celebration,
administered in Europe by Thankyou Music,
PO Box 75, Eastbourne, East Sussex BN23 6NW, UK

and to a - bide in Me_____ is to be real-ly free.

Optional descant for refrain

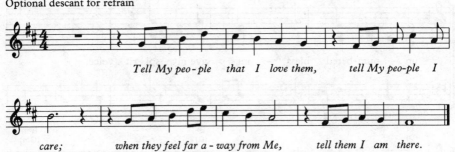

Tell My peo-ple that I love them, tell My peo-ple I

care; when they feel far a-way from Me, tell them I am there.

Tell My people I love them,
tell My people I care;
when they feel far away from Me,
tell My people I am there.

1 Tell My people I came and died
   to give them liberty;
   and to abide in Me
   is to be really free.
     Tell my people . . .

2 Tell My people where'er they go
   My comfort they can know;
   My peace and joy and love
   I freely will bestow.
     Tell my people . . .

631(i) Tell out, my soul

Go Forth   10 10 10 10

Words: Timothy Dudley-Smith
Music: Michael Baughen

With a swing

1 Tell out, my soul, the greatness of the Lord;
   unnumbered blessings give my spirit voice;
   tender to me the promise of His word;
   in God my Saviour shall my heart rejoice.

2 Tell out, my soul, the greatness of His name!
   Make known His might, the deeds His arm has done;
   His mercy sure, from age to age the same;
   His Holy name – the Lord, the Mighty One.

631 (ii) Tell out, my soul

WOODLANDS 10 10 10 10

Words: Timothy Dudley-Smith
Music: W Greatorex (1877–1949)

3 Tell out, my soul, the greatness of His might!
   powers and dominions lay their glory by;
   proud hearts and stubborn wills are put to flight,
   the hungry fed, the humble lifted high.

4 Tell out, my soul, the glories of His word!
   firm is His promise, and His mercy sure:
   tell out, my soul, the greatness of the Lord
   to children's children and for evermore!

632   Thank You for the cross

Words and music: Graham Kendrick

Thank You for the cross, the price You paid for us, how You
Now our sins are gone, all for - giv - en, cov - ered

gave Your - self so com - plete - ly, pre - cious Lord, pre - cious Lord.
by Your blood, all for - got - ten, thank You Lord, thank You Lord.

Oh I love You Lord, real - ly love You Lord. I will

ne - ver un - der - stand why You love me.__ You're my deep - est joy,__ You're my

heart's de-light, and the great-est thing of all, O Lord, I

see: You de-light in me!

1 Thank You for the cross,
   the price You paid for us,
   how You gave Yourself
   so completely,
   precious Lord, precious Lord.
   Now our sins are gone,
   all forgiven,
   covered by Your blood,
   all forgotten,
   thank You Lord, thank You Lord.
     Oh I love You Lord,
     really love You Lord.
     I will never understand
     why You love me.
     You're my deepest joy,
     You're my heart's delight,
     and the greatest thing of all,
     O Lord, I see:
     You delight in me!

2 For our healing there
   Lord You suffered,
   and to take our fear
   You poured out Your love,
   precious Lord, precious Lord.
   Calvary's work is done,
   You have conquered,
   able now to save
   so completely,
   thank You Lord, thank You Lord.
     Oh I love You . . .

633 Thank You Jesus

Words and music: Alison Huntley
Music arranged Roland Fudge

2 You went to Calvary, there You died for me,
   thank You Lord for loving me.
   You went to Calvary . . .

3 You rose up from the grave, to me new life You gave,
   thank You Lord for loving me.
   You rose up from the grave . . .

4 You're coming back again, and we with You shall reign,
   thank You Lord for loving me.
   You're coming back again . . .

634   Thank You, Jesus, for Your love

Words and music: Alison Huntley
Music arranged Christopher Norton

Thank You, Je-sus,_____ for Your love to me;_____ thank You, Je-sus,_____ for Your grace so free._____ I'll lift my voice to praise Your name, praise You a-gain and a-gain: You are ev-ery-thing,_____ You are my Lord._____

635 Thank You Lord

Words and music: Greg Leavers
and Phil Burt

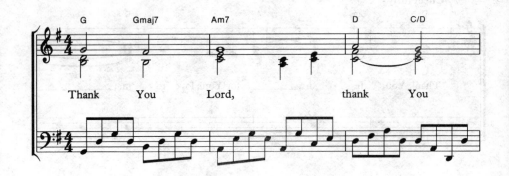

Thank You Lord, thank You

Lord that no - thing can se - pa - rate us

from Your love.

1 Thank You Lord, thank You Lord
   that nothing can separate us from Your love.

2 Thank You Lord, thank You Lord
   that there is no condemnation when we're in You.

CONFESSION VERSES
3 Search my heart, search my heart,
   and show me the sin I need to confess to You.

4 Sorry Lord, sorry Lord,
   I humbly now ask forgiveness for my sin.

5 Cleanse me Lord, cleanse me Lord,
   through Your precious blood make my heart clean before You.

6 Thank You Lord, thank You Lord
   that You've now removed the guilt of all my sin.

COMMUNION
7 Take this bread, take this bread,
   for this is Christ's body which was broken for you.

8 Thank You Lord, thank You Lord
   for dying on Calvary so that I can know You.

9 Take this cup, take this cup
   and drink it remembering Jesus Christ died for you.

10 Thank You Lord, thank You Lord,
   that through Your shed blood we are made one with God.

PRAISE AND WORSHIP
11 Fill me Lord, fill me Lord,
   so that I might learn to live through Your power alone.

12 We love You, we love You,
   we open our hearts in adoration to You.

13 Holy Lord, holy Lord,
   Your name is far higher than any other name.

14 Worthy Lord, worthy Lord,
   we offer our sacrifice of worship to You.

15 Reigning King, reigning King,
   You're glorious in majesty, almighty in power.

636 Thank You Lord, for Your presence

Words and music: Roland Fudge

Guitar: Tune 6th string to D

Thank You Lord, for Your presence here,
thank You Lord, thank You Lord.
Thank You Lord, You remove all fear,
thank You Lord, thank You Lord.
For the love that You showed
as You poured out Your life,
we thank You, we bless You,
Christ Jesus our Lord,
we thank You Lord, thank You Lord.
Thank You Lord . . .

637 Thanks be to God

Words and music: Robert Stoodley

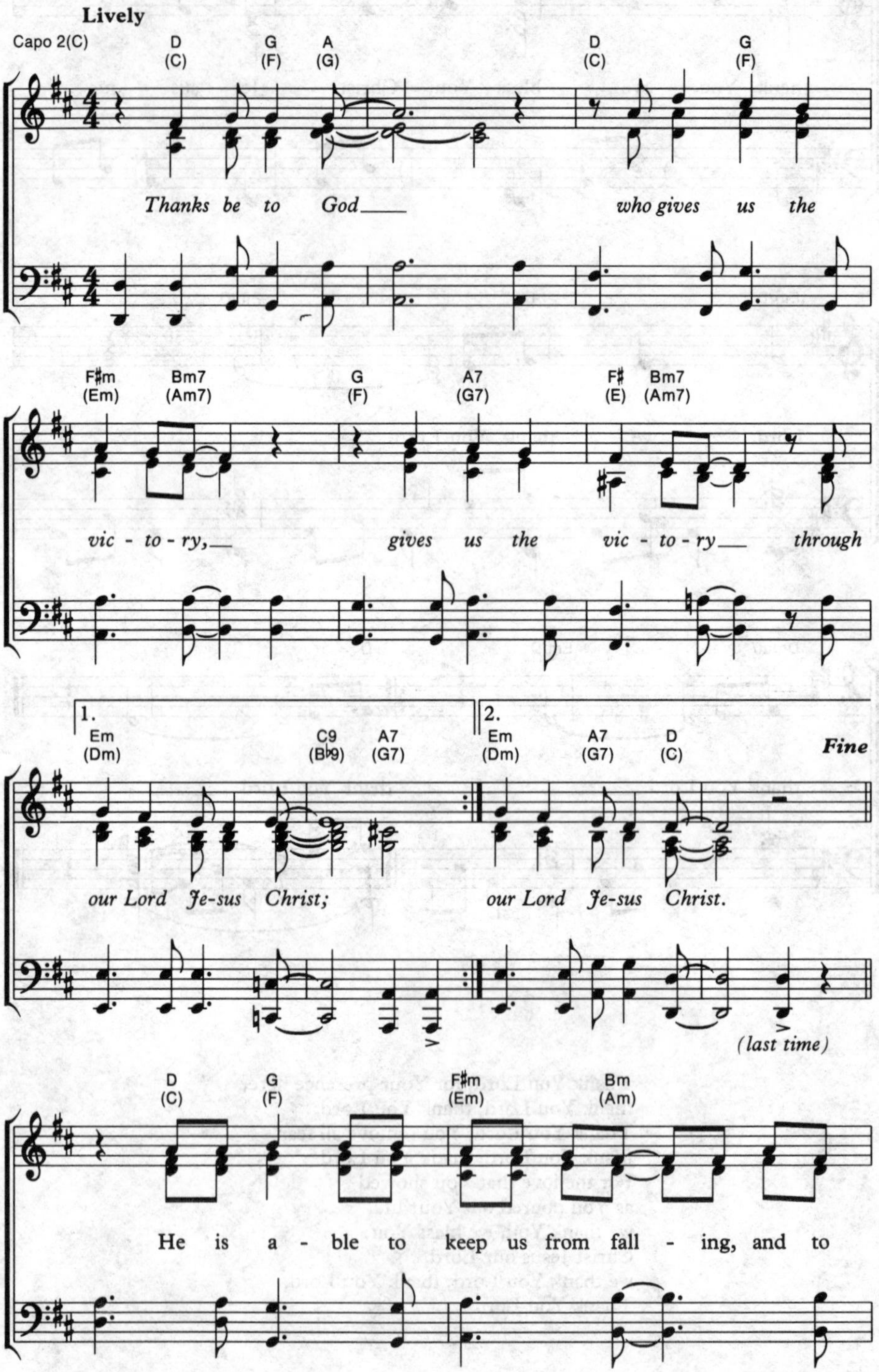
Lively
Capo 2(C)
D (C) G (F) A (G) D (C) G (F)
Thanks be to God___ who gives us the
F♯m (Em) Bm7 (Am7) G (F) A7 (G7) F♯ (E) Bm7 (Am7)
vic - to - ry,___ gives us the vic - to - ry___ through
1. Em (Dm) C9 (B♭9) A7 (G7)
our Lord Je-sus Christ;
2. Em (Dm) A7 (G7) D (C)
our Lord Je-sus Christ.
Fine
(last time)
D (C) G (F) F♯m (Em) Bm (Am)
He is a - ble to keep us from fall - ing, and to

set us free from sin:___ so let us each live
up to our call-ing, and com-mit our way_____ to Him._

Thanks be to God
 who gives us the victory,
gives us the victory
 through our Lord Jesus Christ;
thanks be to God
 who gives us the victory,
gives us the victory
 through our Lord Jesus Christ.

1 He is able to keep us from falling,
 and to set us free from sin:
 so let us each live up to our calling,
 and commit our way to Him.
  Thanks be to God . . .

2 Jesus knows all about our temptations –
 He has had to bear them too;
 He will show us how to escape them,
 if we trust Him He will lead us through.
  Thanks be to God . . .

3 He has led us from the power of darkness
 to the kingdom of His blessèd Son:
 so let us join in praise together,
 and rejoice in what the Lord has done.
  Thanks be to God . . .

4 Praise the Lord for sending Jesus
 to the cross of Calvary:
 now He's risen, reigns in power,
 and death is swallowed up in victory.
  Thanks be to God . . .

638 Thank You God, for sending Jesus

Words and music: Unknown
Music arranged Phil Burt

Thank You God, for send-ing Je - sus;
thank You Je-sus, that You came; Ho - ly Spi-rit, won't You
teach us more a - bout His won-drous name?

Thank You God, for sending Jesus;
thank You Jesus, that You came;
Holy Spirit, won't You teach us
more about His wondrous name?

639   The battle belongs to the Lord

Words and music: Jamie Owens-Collins
Music arranged Christopher Norton

Rock feel

1 In hea-ven-ly ar - mour we'll en-
(2) pow-er of dark-ness comes in
(3) e-ne-my press-es in hard,

-ter the land
like a flood, the bat-tle be-longs to the Lord;
do not fear

no wea-pon that's fash-ioned a-gainst
He's raised up a stan-dard, the power
take cour-age, my friend, your re-demp-

Words and music: © 1984 Fairhill Music (USA)/Word Music (UK), (a division of Word (UK) Ltd)
9 Holdom Avenue, Bletchley, Milton Keynes MK1 1QR, UK

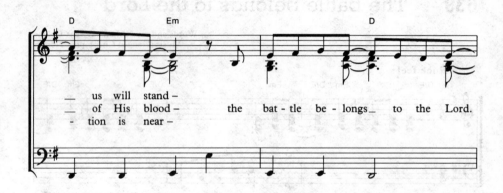

_us will stand–
of His blood– the bat-tle be-longs to the Lord.
-tion is near–

_ We sing glo - ry, hon - our,

pow-er and strength to the Lord;_ we sing glo - ry,

hon - our, pow-er and strength to the Lord!_

640 The Church's one foundation

AURELIA 76 76 D

Words: Samuel John Stone (1839–1900)
Music: S S Wesley (1810–76)

The Chur-ch's one foun - da - tion is Je - sus Christ our Lord:

she is His new cre - a - tion by wa - ter and the word;

from heaven He came and sought her to be His ho - ly bride;

with His own blood He bought her, and for her life He died.

1   The Church's one foundation
    is Jesus Christ our Lord:
    she is His new creation
    by water and the word;
    from heaven He came and sought her
    to be His holy bride;
    with His own blood He bought her,
    and for her life He died.

2   Elect from every nation,
    yet one o'er all the earth,
    her charter of salvation
    one Lord, one faith, one birth,
    one holy name she blesses,
    partakes one holy food,
    and to one hope she presses,
    with every grace endued.

3   Though with a scornful wonder
    men see her sore oppressed,
    by schisms rent asunder
    by heresies distressed;
    yet saints their watch are keeping,
    their cry goes up: How long?
    and soon the night of weeping
    shall be the morn of song.

4   Mid toil and tribulation,
    and tumult of her war,
    she waits the consummation
    of peace for evermore;
    till with the vision glorious
    her longing eyes are blest,
    and the great Church victorious
    shall be the Church at rest.

5   Yet she on earth hath union
    with God the Three-in-One,
    and mystic sweet communion
    with those whose rest is won.
    O happy ones and holy!
    Lord, give us grace that we,
    like them, the meek and lowly,
    on high may dwell with Thee.

641 The day Thou gavest

ST CLEMENT   98 98

Words: John Ellerton (1826–93)
Music: C C Scholefield (1839–1904)

The day_ Thou gav - est, Lord, is end-ed, the dark - ness falls_ at Thy_ be - hest; to Thee_ our morn - ing hymns as - cend-ed, Thy praise shall sanc - ti - fy_ our rest.

1 The day Thou gavest, Lord, is ended,
   the darkness falls at Thy behest;
   to Thee our morning hymns ascended,
   Thy praise shall sanctify our rest.

2 We thank Thee that Thy Church unsleeping,
   while earth rolls onward into light,
   through all the world her watch is keeping,
   and rests not now by day or night.

3 As o'er each continent and island
   the dawn leads on another day,
   the voice of prayer is never silent,
   nor dies the strain of praise away.

4 The sun, that bids us rest, is waking
   our brethren 'neath the western sky,
   and hour by hour fresh lips are making
   Thy wondrous doings heard on high.

5 So be it, Lord: Thy throne shall never,
   like earth's proud empires, pass away;
   Thy kingdom stands, and grows for ever,
   till all Thy creatures own Thy sway.

642   The earth is the Lord's

Words and music: Graham Kendrick
Music arranged Christopher Norton

Rhythmically

MEN The earth is the Lord's   MEN The
WOMEN and ev - ery-thing in it.

earth is the Lord's,   MEN The earth is the
WOMEN the work of His hands.

Lord's   ALL and all things were
WOMEN and ev - ery - thing in it,

3rd time **to Coda** ⊕

made for His glo - ry!_____

643 The earth was dark

Words and music: John Daniels
and Phil Thompson

The earth was dark un - til You spoke – then all was light and all was peace; yet still, O God, so ma - ny___ wait to see the flame of love re - leased.___ *Lights to the world! O Light di - vine, kin - dle in us a*

migh-ty flame, till ev-ery heart, con-sumed by love shall rise to___

praise Your ho - ly name!

1 The earth was dark until You spoke –
   then all was light and all was peace;
   yet still, O God, so many wait
   to see the flame of love released.
      Lights to the world! O Light divine,
      kindle in us a mighty flame,
      till every heart, consumed by love
      shall rise to praise Your holy name!

2 In Christ You gave Your gift of life
   to save us from the depth of the night:
   O come and set our spirits free
   and draw us to Your perfect light.
      Lights to the world . . .

3 Where there is fear may we bring joy
   and healing to a world in pain:
   Lord, build Your kingdom through our lives
   till Jesus walks this earth again.
      Lights to the world . . .

4 O burn in us, that we may burn
   with love that triumphs in despair;
   and touch our lives with such a fire
   that souls may search and find You there.
      Lights to the world . . .

644

The first nowell

THE FIRST NOWELL   Irregular

Words: Author unknown (c 17th century)
in this version Jubilate Hymns
Music: English traditional carol
arranged David Willcocks

The_ first____ no - well the_ an - gel did

say, was to Beth - le - hem's shep-herds in fields as they

lay; in_ fields____ where they lay_ keep - ing their

sheep on a cold win-ter's night_ that was_ so deep:

No - well,___ no - well, no - well, no -

- well, born is the king___ of Is - ra - el!

1 The first nowell the angel did say,
   was to Bethlehem's shepherds in fields as they lay;
   in fields where they lay keeping their sheep
   on a cold winter's night that was so deep:
      Nowell, nowell, nowell, nowell,
      born is the king of Israel!

2 Then wise men from a country far
   looked up and saw a guiding star;
   they travelled on by night and day
   to reach the place where Jesus lay:
      Nowell, nowell . . .

3 At Bethlehem they entered in,
   on bended knee they worshipped Him;
   they offered there in His presence
   their gold and myrrh and frankincense:
      Nowell, nowell . . .

4 Then let us all with one accord
   sing praises to our heavenly Lord;
   for Christ has our salvation wrought
   and with His blood mankind has bought:
      Nowell, nowell . . .

645 The God of Abraham praise

Leoni   66 84 D

Words: Thomas Olivers (1725–99) altd.
Music: from a Hebrew melody
Thomas Olivers (1725–99)

The God of Abra-ham praise, who reigns en-throned a-

-bove, An - cient of ev - er - last - ing days, and

God___ of___ love. Je - ho - vah, great I

AM! by___ earth_ and_ heaven con - fessed; we___

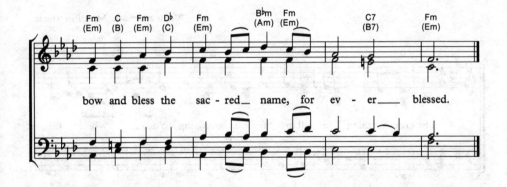

bow and bless the sac-red_ name, for ev-er___ blessed.

1 The God of Abraham praise,
   who reigns enthroned above,
   Ancient of everlasting days,
   and God of love.
   Jehovah, great I AM!
   by earth and heaven confessed;
   we bow and bless the sacred name,
   for ever blessed.

2 The God of Abraham praise,
   at whose supreme command
   from earth we rise, and seek the joys
   at His right hand;
   we all on earth forsake,
   its wisdom, fame, and power;
   and Him our only portion make,
   our shield and tower.

3 The God of Abraham praise,
   whose all-sufficient grace
   shall guide us all our happy days,
   in all our ways:
   He is our faithful friend;
   He is our gracious God;
   and He will save us to the end,
   through Jesus' blood.

4 He by Himself has sworn –
   we on His oath depend –
   we shall, on eagles' wings upborne,
   to heaven ascend:
   we shall behold His face,
   we shall His power adore,
   and sing the wonders of His grace
   for evermore.

5 The whole triumphant host
   give thanks to God on high:
   'Hail, Father, Son, and Holy Ghost!'
   they ever cry.
   Hail, Abraham's God and ours!
   We join the heavenly lays;
   and celebrate with all our powers
   His endless praise.

646 The greatest thing

Words and music: Mark Pendergras

2 The greatest thing in all my life
   is loving You;
   the greatest thing in all my life
   is loving You;
   I want to love You more;
   I want to love You more.
   The greatest thing in all my life
   is loving You.

3 The greatest thing in all my life
   is serving You;
   the greatest thing in all my life
   is serving You;
   I want to serve You more;
   I want to serve You more.
   The greatest thing in all my life
   is serving You.

647   The head that once was crowned

St Magnus   CM

Words: Thomas Kelly (1769–1855)
Music: J Clark (c1670–1707)

1 The head that once was crowned with thorns
  is crowned with glory now;
  a royal diadem adorns
  the mighty victor's brow.

2 The highest place that heaven affords
  is His by sovereign right;
  the King of kings and Lord of lords,
  He reigns in perfect light.

3 The joy of all who dwell above,
  the joy of all below,
  to whom He manifests His love,
  and grants His name to know.

4 To them the cross, with all its shame,
  with all its grace is given;
  their name an everlasting name,
  their joy the joy of heaven.

5 They suffer with their Lord below;
  they reign with Him above;
  their profit and their joy, to know
  The mystery of His love.

6 The cross He bore is life and health,
  though shame and death to Him:
  His people's hope, His people's wealth,
  their everlasting theme.

648   The heavens declare

Words and music: Andy Silver

649

The King of love

DOMINUS REGIT ME   87 87

Words: Henry Williams Baker (1821–77)
Music: John Bacchus Dykes (1823–76)

The King of__ love my__ Shep - herd is, whose
good - ness fail - eth ne - ver; I no - thing lack if
I am__ His and__ He is mine for ev - er.

1 The King of love my Shepherd is,
  whose goodness faileth never;
  I nothing lack if I am His
  and He is mine for ever.

2 Where streams of living water flow
  my ransomed soul He leadeth,
  and where the verdant pastures grow
  with food celestial feedeth.

3 Perverse and foolish oft I strayed;
  but yet in love He sought me,
  and on His shoulder gently laid,
  and home rejoicing brought me.

4 In death's dark vale I fear no ill
  with Thee, dear Lord, beside me;
  Thy rod and staff my comfort still,
  Thy cross before to guide me.

5 Thou spread'st a table in my sight;
  Thy unction grace bestoweth;
  and O what transport of delight
  from Thy pure chalice floweth!

6 And so through all the length of days
  Thy goodness faileth never;
  Good Shepherd, may I sing Thy praise
  within Thy house for ever!

The King is among us

Words and music: Graham Kendrick
Music arranged Chris Rolinson

The King is a - mong us,___ His Spi - rit is here:___ let's draw near and wor - - -

1 The King is among us,
His Spirit is here:
let's draw near and worship,
let songs fill the air!

2 He looks down upon us,
delight in His face,
enjoying His children's love,
enthralled by our praise.

3 For each child is special,
accepted and loved –
a love gift from Jesus
to His Father above.

4 And now He is giving
His gifts to us all;
for no one is worthless
and each one is called.

5 The Spirit's anointing
on all flesh comes down,
and we shall be channels
for works like His own:

6 We come now believing
Your promise of power,
for we are Your people
and this is Your hour.

651 The kingdom of God

HANOVER   10 10 11 11

Words: Bryn Rees (1911–83)
Music: *A New Supplement to the New Version*, 1708

The king-dom of God is jus-tice and joy,

for Je-sus re-stores what sin would de-stroy;

God's pow-er and glo-ry in Je-sus we know,

and here and here-af-ter the king-dom shall grow.

1 The kingdom of God
    is justice and joy,
for Jesus restores
    what sin would destroy;
God's power and glory
    in Jesus we know,
and here and hereafter
    the kingdom shall grow.

2 The kingdom of God
    is mercy and grace,
the captives are freed,
    the sinners find place,
the outcast are welcomed
    God's banquet to share,
and hope is awakened
    in place of despair.

3 The kingdom of God
    is challenge and choice,
believe the good news,
    repent and rejoice!
His love for us sinners
    brought Christ to His cross,
our crisis of judgement
    for gain or for loss.

4 God's kingdom is come,
    the gift and the goal,
in Jesus begun,
    in heaven made whole;
the heirs of the kingdom
    shall answer His call,
and all things cry glory
    to God all in all!

652   The light of Christ

Words and music: Donald Fishel
Music arranged Betty Pulkingham

Flowing

Part 1 *The light of Christ has*

Part 2 *The light of Christ*

come in - to the world; the light of

has come in - to the world; the

last time **to Coda** ⊕

Christ has come in - to the world.

light of Christ has come.

1 All men must be born a-gain to see the King-dom of
2 God gave up His on-ly Son out of love for the
3 The light of God has come to us so that we might have sal -

God; the wa - ter and the Spi - rit bring new
world, so that all men who be - lieve in Him will
- va - tion; from the dark - ness of our sins we walk in - to

CODA

D.C.

life in God's love. world.
live for ev - er.
glo - ry with Christ Je - sus.

653 The Lord has given

Words and music: Unknown
Music arranged Phil Burt

The Lord has giv - en___ a land of good things, I will press
on___ and make them mine;___ I'll know His pow - er,___ I'll know His
glo - ry,___ and in His king - dom I will shine. *With the*
high   prais-es of God in our mouth, and a   two-edged sword in our

hand, we'll march right on to the vic - to - ry side,___

right in - to Ca - naan's land.___

1   The Lord has given a land of good things,
     I will press on and make them mine;
     I'll know His power, I'll know His glory,
     and in His kingdom I will shine.
       With the high praises of God in our mouth,
       and a two-edged sword in our hand,
       we'll march right on to the victory side,
       right into Canaan's land.

2   Gird up your armour, ye sons of Zion,
     gird up your armour, let's go to war;
     we'll win the battle with great rejoicing
     and so we'll praise Him more and more.
       With the high praises . . .

3   We'll bind their kings in chains and fetters,
     we'll bind their nobles tight in iron,
     to execute God's written judgement –
     march on to glory, sons of Zion!
       With the high praises . . .

654 The Lord has led forth

Words and music: Chris Bowater
Music arranged Phil Burt

The Lord has led forth His peo-ple with joy, and His cho-sen ones with sing - ing, sing - ing; the Lord has led forth His peo-ple with joy, and His cho-sen ones with sing - - ing.

Fine

He has given to them___ the lands of the na-

-tions, to pos - sess the fruit and keep His laws, and praise,___

Em7 *G/A* *A7* **D.$ al Fine**

___ praise His name.___ The

The Lord has led forth His people with joy,
and His chosen ones with singing, singing;
the Lord has led forth His people with joy,
and His chosen ones with singing.
He has given to them the lands of the nations,
to possess the fruit and keep His laws,
and praise, praise His name.
The Lord has led forth His people with joy,
and His chosen ones with singing, singing;
the Lord has led forth His people with joy,
and His chosen ones with singing.

655 The Lord is a great and mighty King

Words and music: Diane Davis

1 We are His voice, we His song;
2 We are His bo - dy here on earth;
3 For our Lord_ we will stand,
4 The Lord our God_ is_ one,

let us praise Him all day long.
from a - bove He gave us birth.
sent by Him to ev - ery land.
Fa - ther, Spi - rit, and the Son.

Al - le - lu - ia._ The

The Lord is a great and mighty King,
just and gentle with everything;
so with happiness we sing,
and let His praises ring.

1 We are His voice, we His song;
   let us praise Him all day long. Alleluia.
   The Lord is a great . . .

2 We are His body here on earth;
   from above He gave us birth. Alleluia.
   The Lord is a great . . .

3 For our Lord we will stand,
   sent by Him to every land. Alleluia.
   The Lord is a great . . .

4 The Lord our God is one,
   Father, Spirit, and the Son. Alleluia.
   The Lord is a great . . .

656(i) The Lord is King!

CHURCH TRIUMPHANT   LM

Words: Josiah Conder (1789–1855)
Music: J W Elliott (1833–1915)

1 The Lord is King! lift up thy voice,
   O earth, and all ye heavens rejoice;
   from world to world the joy shall ring,
   'The Lord omnipotent is King!'

2 The Lord is King! who then shall dare
   resist His will, distrust His care,
   or murmur at His wise decrees,
   or doubt His royal promises?

3 The Lord is King! Child of the dust,
   the Judge of all the earth is just;
   holy and true are all His ways:
   let every creature speak His praise.

4 He reigns! ye saints, exalt your strains;
   your God is King, your Father reigns;
   and He is at the Father's side,
   the man of love, the crucified.

5 One Lord, one empire, all secures;
   He reigns, and life and death are yours,
   through earth and heaven one song shall ring,
   'The Lord omnipotent is King!'

656(ii) The Lord is King!

NIAGARA   LM

Words: Josiah Conder (1789–1855)
Music: R Jackson (1840–1914)

The Lord is King! lift up thy voice, O earth, and
all ye heavens re - joice; from world to world the joy shall
ring, 'The Lord om - ni - po - tent is King!'

1 The Lord is King! lift up thy voice,
O earth, and all ye heavens rejoice;
from world to world the joy shall ring,
'The Lord omnipotent is King!'

2 The Lord is King! who then shall dare
resist His will, distrust His care,
or murmur at His wise decrees,
or doubt His royal promises?

3 The Lord is King! Child of the dust,
the Judge of all the earth is just;
holy and true are all His ways:
let every creature speak His praise.

4 He reigns! ye saints, exalt your strains;
your God is King, your Father reigns;
and He is at the Father's side,
the man of love, the crucified.

5 One Lord, one empire, all secures;
He reigns, and life and death are yours,
through earth and heaven one song shall ring,
'The Lord omnipotent is King!'

657 The Lord is King

Words and music: Graham Kendrick

Triumphantly

The Lord is King, He is migh-ty in bat-tle, work-ing won-ders, glor-ious in ma - jes - ty. The Lord is King – so ma - jes - tic in pow - er! His right hand has shat-tered the e - ne - my.

658 The Lord is my strength

Words and music: Roland Fudge

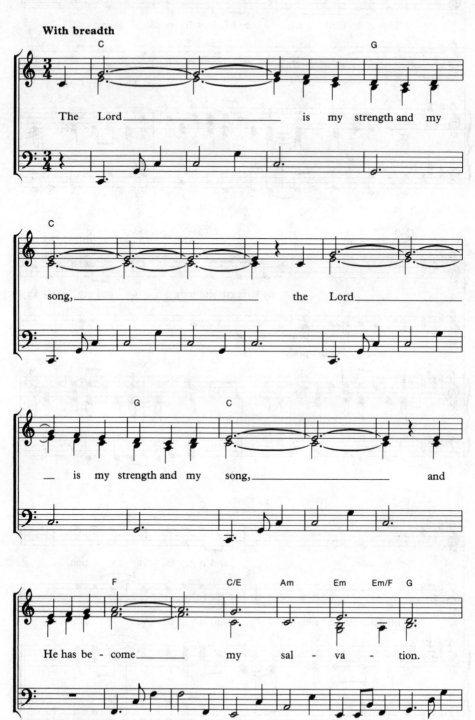

With breadth

The Lord_____ is my strength and my song,_____ the Lord_____ is my strength and my song,_____ and He has be - come_____ my sal - va - tion.

He has done mar-vel-lous things._____ The Lord_____ is my strength and my song,_____ the Lord_____ is my strength and my song,_____ and He has be-come my sal-va-tion._____

The Lord reigns

Words and music: Angela Pack

Steadily

The Lord reigns,_____ the Lord

reigns,_____ He is robed_____

_____ in ma - jes - ty,_____ the Lord is

robed _____ in ma - jes - ty,_____

and He is gird - ed with

strength. The Lord has es-

-tab - lished the world,

it shall ne - ver be moved;

The Lord reigns, the Lord reigns,
He is robed in majesty,
the Lord is robed in majesty,
and He is girded with strength.

1   The Lord has established the world,
    it shall never be moved;
    Thy throne is established of old,
    Thou art from everlasting.
       The Lord reigns . . .

2   The floods have lifted up, O Lord,
    lifted up their voice;
    mightier than the thunder of the waves,
    the Lord on high is mighty.
       The Lord reigns . . .

660 The Lord's my Shepherd

CRIMOND CM

Words: Francis Rous (1579–1659)
revised for *Scottish Psalter*, 1650
Music: melody by Jessie S Irvine (1836–87)

The Lord's my Shep - herd, I'll not want;

He makes me down to lie

in pas - tures green; He lead - eth me

the qui - et wa - ters by.

1 The Lord's my Shepherd, I'll not want;
  He makes me down to lie
  in pastures green; He leadeth me
  the quiet waters by.

2 My soul He doth restore again,
  and me to walk doth make
  within the paths of righteousness,
  e'en for His own name's sake.

3 Yea, though I walk through death's dark vale,
  yet will I fear none ill;
  for Thou art with me, and Thy rod
  and staff me comfort still.

4 My table Thou hast furnished
  in presence of my foes;
  my head Thou dost with oil anoint,
  and my cup overflows.

5 Goodness and mercy all my life
  shall surely follow me;
  and in God's house for evermore
  my dwelling-place shall be.

661 The Lord's Prayer

Music: Joseph Lees

662 The love of Christ who died for me

Words: Timothy Dudley-Smith
Music: Phil Burt

The love of Christ who died for me

is more than mind can_ know,_____

His mer - cy mea - sure-less and free to_

meet the debt I owe._____

1   The love of Christ who died for me
     is more than mind can know,
     His mercy measureless and free
     to meet the debt I owe.

2   He came my sinful cause to plead,
     He laid His glories by,
     for me a homeless life to lead,
     a shameful death to die.

3   My sins I only see in part,
     my self-regarding ways;
     the secret places of my heart
     lie bare before His gaze.

4   For me the price of sin He paid;
     my sins beyond recall
     are all alike on Jesus laid,
     He died to bear them all.

5   O living Lord of life, for whom
     the heavens held their breath,
     to see, triumphant from the tomb,
     a love that conquers death.

6   Possess my heart that it may be
     Your kingdom without end,
     O Christ who died for love of me
     and lives to be my friend.

663 The price is paid

Words and music: Graham Kendrick
Music arranged David Peacock

Unhurried

The price is paid: come, let us en-ter in to all that
Je-sus died to make our own. For ev-ery sin more than e-nough He
gave, and bought our free-dom from each guil-ty stain. *The price is*
paid, Al-le-lu - ia- a-maz-ing grace, *so strong and sure!* And so with

all my heart, my life in ev-ery part,_ I live to thank You for_ the price You paid.

The price is

1 The price is paid:
      come, let us enter in
   to all that Jesus died
      to make our own.
   For every sin
      more than enough He gave,
   and bought our freedom
      from each guilty stain.
   The price is paid, Alleluia –
   amazing grace,
   so strong and sure!
   And so with all my heart,
   my life in every part,
   I live to thank You
   for the price You paid.

2 The price is paid:
      see Satan flee away –
   for Jesus, crucified,
      destroys his power.
   No more to pay!
      Let accusation cease:
   in Christ there is
      no condemnation now!
   The price is paid, . . .

3 The price is paid:
      and by that scourging cruel,
   He took our sicknesses
      as if His own.
   And by His wounds,
      His body broken there,
   His healing touch may now
      by faith be known.
   The price is paid, . . .

4 The price is paid:
      'Worthy the Lamb!' we cry –
   eternity shall never
      cease His praise.
   The Church of Christ
      shall rule upon the earth:
   in Jesus' name
      we have authority!
   The price is paid, . . .

664 The Spirit lives

WALK IN THE LIGHT

Words and music: Damien Lundy

The Spi-rit lives to set us free, walk, walk in the light; He

binds us all in u-ni-ty, walk, walk in the light.

Walk in the light,_ walk in the light,_

walk in the light,_ walk in the light of the Lord.

1   The Spirit lives to set us free,
       walk, walk in the light;
    He binds us all in unity,
       walk, walk in the light.
          Walk in the light,
          walk in the light,
          walk in the light,
          walk in the light of the Lord.

2   Jesus promised life to all,
       walk, walk in the light;
    the dead were wakened by His call,
       walk, walk in the light.
          Walk in the light . . .

3   He died in pain on Calvary,
       walk, walk in the light;
    to save the lost like you and me,
       walk, walk in the light.
          Walk in the light . . .

4   We know His death was not the end,
       walk, walk in the light;
    He gave His Spirit to be our friend,
       walk, walk in the light.
          Walk in the light . . .

5   By Jesus' love our wounds are healed,
       walk, walk in the light;
    the Father's kindness is revealed,
       walk, walk in the light.
          Walk in the light . . .

6   The Spirit lives in you and me,
       walk, walk in the light;
    His light will shine for all to see,
       walk, walk in the light.
          Walk in the light . . .

665 The Spirit of the Lord

Words and music: Chris Bowater

1 The Spi - rit of the
2 And He has called on
3 Let right-eous-ness a -

Lord, the sove - reign Lord, is on_____ me
me to bind up all the bro - ken hearts,
- rise and blos - som as a gar - den;

be-cause He has a - noint - ed me to preach good news___
to mi - ni - ster re - lease to ev - ery cap - ti - va - ted
let praise be - gin to spring in ev - ery tongue_ and_

to the poor:_____
soul:_____
na - tion:_____ *Pro-claim-ing Je* - -

sus, on-ly Je - - - sus — it is Je - sus, Sav-iour,

heal-er and bap-tiz-er, and the migh - ty King, the vic-tor and de-liv-erer — He is

Lord, He is Lord, He is Lord.

1 The Spirit of the Lord,
   the sovereign Lord, is on me,
   because He has anointed me
   to preach good news to the poor:
   Proclaiming Jesus, only Jesus –
   it is Jesus, Saviour, healer and baptizer,
   and the mighty King, the victor and deliverer –
   He is Lord, He is Lord, He is Lord.

2 And He has called on me
   to bind up all the broken hearts,
   to minister release to every
   captivated soul:
   Proclaiming Jesus . . .

3 Let righteousness arise
   and blossom as a garden;
   let praise begin to spring in every
   tongue and nation:
   Proclaiming Jesus . . .

666 The steadfast love

Words and music: Edith McNeill

With a rocking rhythm

Capo 4(C)

The stead-fast love of the Lord ne-ver ceas - es, His mer-cies ne - ver come to an end; they are new ev-ery morn-ing, new ev-ery morn-ing: great is Thy faith-ful - ness, O Lord, great is Thy faith-ful - ness.

Fine | Verse 1

1 The Lord is my por-tion, says my

The guitar chords and piano arrangement are not designed to be used together.

Words and music: © 1974, 1975 Celebration,
administered in Europe by Thankyou Music,
PO Box 75, Eastbourne, East Sussex BN23 6NW, UK

667 The trumpets sound

Words and music: Graham Kendrick
Music arranged Christopher Norton

The trum-pets sound, the an-gels sing, the feast is rea-dy to be-gin; the gates of heaven are o-pen wide, and Je-sus wel-comes you in-side.

Sing with thank-ful-ness songs of pure de-light, come and re-vel in hea-ven's love and light;

1 The trumpets sound, the angels sing,
   the feast is ready to begin;
   the gates of heaven are open wide,
   and Jesus welcomes you inside.
   The trumpets sound . . .
       Sing with thankfulness songs of pure delight,
       come and revel in heaven's love and light;
       take your place at the table of the King,
       the feast is ready to begin,
       the feast is ready to begin.

2 Tables are laden with good things,
   O taste the peace and joy He brings;
   He'll fill you up with love divine,
   He'll turn your water into wine.
       Sing with thankfulness . . .

3 The hungry heart He satisfies,
   offers the poor His paradise;
   now hear all heaven and earth applaud
   the amazing goodness of the Lord.
       Sing with thankfulness . . .

668 The world was in darkness

RICH AND FREE   10 9 10 10 with refrain

Words: verses 1 and 2 Seth Sykes
verse 3 Glyn L Taylor
Music: Richard Maxwell, William Wirges
and Seth Sykes

The world was in dark-ness in sin and shame;

man-kind was lost, and then Je-sus came. He car-ried our sins to

Cal-va-ry's tree, He hung there, and bled there, for you and me.

Thank You Lord, for sav-ing my soul. Thank You Lord, for

mak-ing me whole. Thank You Lord, for giv-ing to me,____

Thy great sal-va-tion so rich____ and free.

1 The world was in darkness in sin and shame;
mankind was lost, and then Jesus came.
He carried our sins to Calvary's tree,
He hung there, and bled there, for you and me.
    Thank You Lord, for saving my soul.
    Thank You Lord, for making me whole.
    Thank You Lord, for giving to me
    Thy great salvation so rich and free.

2 Lord Jesus came down from His throne on high;
ready to live and willing to die.
For all of the pain and the suffering He bore,
I'll love Him and thank Him for evermore.
    Thank You Lord . . .

3 To You I surrender my all today,
the debt I owe, I ne'er could repay,
I'll serve You with joy wherever You lead,
with this great assurance, You'll meet my need.
    Thank You Lord . . .

669   Then I saw a new heaven and earth

Words: Christopher Idle
Music: Norman Warren

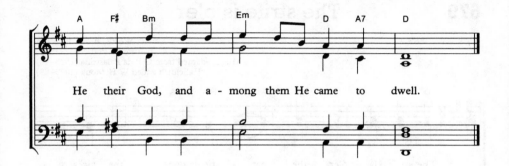

He their God, and a - mong them He came to dwell.

1   Then I saw a new heaven and earth,
    for the first had passed away;
    and the holy city, come down from God,
    like a bride on her wedding day:
    and I know how He loves His own,
    for I heard His great voice tell,
    they would be His people, and He their God,
    and among them He came to dwell.

2   He will wipe away every tear,
    even death shall die at last;
    there'll be no more crying, or grief, or pain,
    they belong to the world that's past:
    and the One on the throne said 'Look!
    I am making all things new';
    He is A and Z, He is first and last,
    and His words are exact and true.

3   So the thirsty can drink their fill
    at the fountain giving life;
    but the gates are shut on all evil things,
    on deceit and decay and strife:
    with foundations and walls and towers,
    like a jewel the city shines;
    with its streets of gold and its gates of pearl,
    in a glory where each combines.

4   As they measured its length and breadth
    I could see no temple there,
    for its only temple is God the Lord
    and the Lamb in that city fair:
    and it needs neither sun nor moon
    in a place which knows no night,
    for the city's lamp is the Lamb Himself
    and the glory of God its light.

5   And I saw by the sacred throne
    flowing water, crystal clear;
    and the tree of life with its healing leaves
    and its fruit growing all the year:
    so the worshippers of the Lamb
    bear His name, and see His face;
    and they reign and serve and for ever live
    to the praise of His glorious grace.

670   The strife is o'er

VICTORY   888 4

Words: From the Latin
tr. Francis Pott (1832–1909)
Music: adapted from G P da Palastrina (1525–94)
Hallelujah added W H Monk (1823–89)

The strife is o'er, the bat - tle done; the vic - to -
- ry of life___ is won; the song of tri - umph
has___ be - gun: Hal - le - lu - jah!

1 The strife is o'er, the battle done;
the victory of life is won;
the song of triumph has begun:
Hallelujah!

2 The powers of death have done their worst,
but Christ their legions has dispersed;
let shouts of holy joy outburst:
Hallelujah!

3 The three sad days have quickly sped:
He rises glorious from the dead;
all glory to our risen Head:
Hallelujah!

4 He broke the bonds of death and hell;
the bars from heaven's high portals fell;
let hymns of praise His triumph tell:
Hallelujah!

5 Lord, by the stripes which wounded Thee,
from death's dread sting Thy servants free,
that we may live, and sing to Thee;
Hallelujah!

671   There is a fountain

St Mary   CM

Words: William Cowper (1731–1800)
Music: from Pry's *Psalter*, 1621

1   There is a fountain filled with blood
     drawn from Emmanuel's veins;
     and sinners, plunged beneath that flood,
     lose all their guilty stains.

2   The dying thief rejoiced to see
     that fountain in his day;
     and there may I, as vile as he,
     wash all my sins away.

3   Dear dying Lamb! Your precious blood
     shall never lose its power,
     till all the ransomed Church of God
     be saved, to sin no more.

4   E'er since, by faith, I saw the stream
     Your flowing wounds supply,
     redeeming love has been my theme,
     and shall be till I die.

5   Then in a nobler, sweeter song,
     I'll sing Your power to save,
     when this poor lisping, stammering tongue
     lies silent in the grave.

672   There is a name I love to hear

Words: F Whitfield
Music: W H Rudd

love the Sav - iour's name,   O how I love the
love_ the Sav - iour's name, how I love, I love_ the

Sav - iour's name,   the sweet - est   name   on   earth.   (on   earth.)
Sav - iour's name,

1   There is a name I love to hear,
    I love to speak its worth;
    it sounds like music in my ear,
    the sweetest name on earth.
        O how I love the Saviour's name,
        O how I love the Saviour's name,
        O how I love the Saviour's name,
        the sweetest name on earth.

2   It tells me of a Saviour's love,
    who died to set me free;
    it tells me of His precious blood,
    the sinner's perfect plea.
        O how I love ...

3   It tells of one whose loving heart
    can feel my deepest woe,
    who in my sorrow bears a part
    that none can bear below.
        O how I love ...

4   It bids my trembling heart rejoice,
    it dries each rising tear;
    it tells me in a 'still, small voice'
    to trust and never fear.
        O how I love ...

5   Jesus, the name I love so well,
    the name I love to hear!
    No saints on earth its worth can tell,
    no heart conceive how dear!
        O how I love ...

673   There is a Redeemer

Words and music: Melody Green

There is a Re-deem - - er,
Je - sus, God's own Son,_____ pre - cious Lamb of
God, Mes-si-ah, ho - - ly One.
Thank You, O my Fa - ther, for giv-ing us Your

1 There is a Redeemer,
    Jesus, God's own Son,
    precious Lamb of God, Messiah,
    holy One.
       Thank You, O my Father,
       for giving us Your Son,
       and leaving Your Spirit
       till the work on earth is done.

2 Jesus my Redeemer,
    name above all names,
    precious Lamb of God, Messiah,
    O for sinners slain:
       Thank You . . .

3 When I stand in glory
    I will see His face,
    and there I'll serve my King for ever
    in that holy place.
       Thank You . . .

There is a green hill

HORSLEY   CM

Words: Cecil Frances Alexander (1818–95)
Music: W Horsley (1774–1858)

1 There is a green hill far away
   without a city wall,
   where the dear Lord was crucified,
   who died to save us all.

2 We may not know, we cannot tell
   what pains He had to bear;
   but we believe it was for us
   He hung and suffered there.

3 He died that we might be forgiven,
   He died to make us good,
   that we might go at last to heaven,
   saved by His precious blood.

4 There was no other good enough
   to pay the price of sin;
   He only could unlock the gate
   of heaven, and let us in.

5 O dearly, dearly has He loved,
   and we must love Him too,
   and trust in His redeeming blood,
   and try His works to do.

675 There is no condemnation

Words and Music: Joan Parsons
Music arranged Andy Silver
and Christopher Norton

Moderato

There is no con-dem-na-tion for those who are in Christ,____ for the Spi-rit of life in Christ has set me free.____ O He's a-live, He's a-live, He's a-live,____ O He's a-live, He's a-live, He's a-live, praise the Lord.____

2 If the Spirit of Him who raised Christ from the dead
  be born in you, then He will give you life.
  O He's alive, . . .

3 If God be for us, who can be against us?
  For He who sent His Son will freely give us all things.
  O He's alive, . . .

676 There is no love like the love of Jesus

THE LOVE OF JESUS   10 6 10 6 with refrain

Words: W E Littlewood (1831–86)
Music: T E Perkins (1831–1912)

There is no love like the love of Je - sus,
ne - ver to fade or fall, till in - to the fold of the
peace of God_ He has ga - thered us all.

Je - sus' love, pre - cious love, bound-less and pure and free! O

turn to that love, wea-ry wand-ering soul, Je-sus plead - eth with thee.

1 There is no love like the love of Jesus,
   never to fade or fall,
   till into the fold of the peace of God
   He has gathered us all.
      Jesus' love, precious love,
      boundless and pure and free!
      O turn to that love, weary wandering soul,
      Jesus pleadeth with thee.

2 There is no heart like the heart of Jesus,
   filled with a tender love,
   no throb nor throe that our hearts can know
   but He feels it above.
      Jesus' love . . .

3 O let us hark to the voice of Jesus!
   O may we never roam,
   till safe we rest on His loving breast
   in the dear heavenly home.
      Jesus' love . . .

677   There is none holy as the Lord

Words and music: Gary Garrett

Not too slowly

There is none ho-ly as the Lord, there is none be-side Thee; nei-ther is there a-ny rock like our God, there is none ho-ly as the Lord.

678   There's a quiet understanding

Words and music: Tedd Smith

679   There's a light upon the mountains

THERE'S A LIGHT UPON THE MOUNTAINS
15 15 15 15

Words: Henry Burton (1840–1930)
Music: M L Wostenholm (1887–1959)

There's a light up-on the moun-tains, and the day is at the spring, when our eyes shall see the beau-ty and the glo-ry of the King; wea-ry was our heart with wait-ing, and the night-watch seemed so long; but His tri-umph-day is

break-ing, and we hail__ it__ with__ a song.__

1　There's a light upon the mountains, and the day is at the spring,
　　when our eyes shall see the beauty and the glory of the King;
　　weary was our heart with waiting, and the night-watch seemed so long;
　　but His triumph-day is breaking, and we hail it with a song.

2　In the fading of the starlight we can see the coming morn;
　　and the lights of men are paling in the splendours of the dawn:
　　for the eastern skies are glowing as with light of hidden fire,
　　and the hearts of men are stirring with the throbs of deep desire.

3　There's a hush of expectation, and a quiet in the air;
　　and the breath of God is moving in the fervent breath of prayer:
　　for the suffering, dying Jesus is the Christ upon the throne,
　　and the travail of our spirit is the travail of His own.

4　He is breaking down the barriers, He is casting up the way;
　　He is calling for His angels to build up the gates of day:
　　but His angels here are human, not the shining hosts above;
　　for the drum-beats of His army are the heart-beats of our love.

5　Hark! we hear a distant music, and it comes with fuller swell;
　　'tis the triumph-song of Jesus, of our King, Immanuel:
　　Zion, go ye forth to meet Him; and, my soul, be swift to bring
　　all thy sweetness and thy dearest for the triumph of our King!

680 There's a song for all the children

IN MEMORIAM   86 76 76 76

Words: Albert Midlane (1825–1909)
in this version Jubilee Hymns
Music: John Stainer (1840–1901)

There's a song for all the child-ren that makes the hea-vens ring,— a song that ev-en an-gels can ne-ver ne-ver sing;— they praise Him as their Mak-er and see Him glo-ri--fied,— but we can call Him Sav-iour be-cause for us He died.

1   There's a song for all the children
     that makes the heavens ring,
     a song that even angels
     can never never sing;
     they praise Him as their Maker
     and see Him glorified,
     but we can call Him Saviour
     because for us He died.

2   There's a place for all the children
     where Jesus reigns in love,
     a place of joy and freedom
     that nothing can remove;
     a home that is more friendly
     than any home we know,
     where Jesus makes us welcome
     because He loves us so.

3   There's a friend for all the children
     to guide us every day,
     whose care is always faithful
     and never fades away;
     there's no-one else so loyal –
     His friendship stays the same;
     He knows us and He loves us,
     and Jesus is His name.

681   There's a sound

BATTLE HYMN   Words and music: Graham Kendrick

1. There's a sound on the wind like a victory song;
   listen now, let it rest on your soul.
   It's a song that I learned from a heavenly King,
   it's a song of a battle royal.

2. There's a loud shout of victory that leaps from our hearts,
   as we wait for our conquering King.
   There's a triumph resounding from dark ages past,
   to the victory song we now sing.
   Come on heaven's children,
   the city is in sight.
   There will be no sadness
   on the other side.

3. There'll be crowns for the conquerors and white robes to wear,
   there will be no more sorrow or pain;
   and the battles of earth shall be lost in the sight,
   of the glorious Lamb that was slain.

4. Now the King of the ages approaches the earth,
   He will burst through the gates of the sky;
   and all men shall bow down to His beautiful name;
   we shall rise with a shout, we shall fly!
   Come on . . .

(repeat verse 4)

682   There's a way back

Words and music: E H Swinstead

There's a way back to God from the dark paths of sin; there's a
door that is o-pen and you may go in: at Cal-va-ry's cross is
where you be-gin, when you come as a sin-ner to Je - sus.

683 There's a wideness in God's mercy

CROSS OF JESUS   87 87

Words: Frederick William Faber (1814–63) altd.
Music: John Stainer (1840–1901)

There's a wide-ness in God's mer-cy__ like the wide-ness of the sea;__

there's a__ kind-ness in His jus-tice which is__ more than li-ber-ty.

1 There's a wideness in God's mercy
   like the wideness of the sea;
   there's a kindness in His justice
   which is more than liberty.

2 There is plentiful redemption
     in the blood that has been shed;
   there is joy for all the members
     in the sorrows of the Head.

3 There is grace enough for thousands
     of new worlds as great as this;
   there is room for fresh creations
     in that upper home of bliss.

4 For the love of God is broader
     than the measures of man's mind;
   and the heart of the Eternal
     is most wonderfully kind.

5 But we make His love too narrow
     by false limits of our own;
   and we magnify His strictness
     with a zeal He will not own.

6 If our love were but more simple
     we should take Him at His word;
   and our lives would be illumined
     by the presence of our Lord.

684   There's no greater name

Words and music: Michael Baughen

1 There's no great - er name than Je - sus,
name of Him who came to save___ us; in that
sav - ing name so gra - cious ev - ery
knee___ shall bow.___

3 In our minds, by faith pro - fess - ing,
in our hearts, by in - ward bless - ing, on our
tongues, by words con - fess - ing, Je - sus
Christ is Lord.___

1 There's no greater name than Jesus,
name of Him who came to save us;
in that saving name so gracious
every knee shall bow.

2 Let everything that's beneath the ground,
let everything in the world around,
let everything exalted on high
bow at Jesus' name.

3 In our minds, by faith professing,
in our hearts, by inward blessing,
on our tongues, by words confessing,
Jesus Christ is Lord.

685 Therefore the redeemed

Words and music: Ruth Lake
Music arranged Christopher Norton

With a swing

Capo 3(G)

There - fore the re - deemed of the Lord shall re -
- turn,___ and come with sing - ing___ un - to Zi - on,___ and ev - er -
- last - ing___ joy shall be up - on their head. There - fore the re -
head. They shall ob - tain_____ glad-ness and

686 Therefore we lift our hearts

Words and music: Colin Green
Music arranged Norman Warren

There - fore we lift our hearts in praise, sing to the

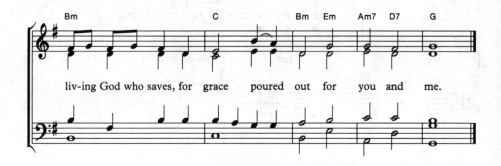

liv-ing God who saves, for grace poured out for you and me.

1 Therefore we lift our hearts in praise,
   sing to the living God who saves,
   for grace poured out for you and me.

2 There for everyone to see,
   there on the hill at Calvary,
   Jesus died for you and me.

3 There for sad and broken men
   He rose up from the grave again,
   and reigns on high for you and me.

4 There for such great pain and cost
   the Spirit came at Pentecost,
   and comes in power for you and me.

5 Therefore we lift our hearts in praise,
   sing to the living God who saves,
   for grace poured out for you and me.

687 These are the facts

YVONNE   10 10 11 10

Words: Michael Saward
Music: Norman Warren

These are the facts as we have re-ceived them, these are the truths that the Chris-tian be-lieves, this is the ba-sis of all of our preach-ing: Christ died for sin-ners and rose from the tomb.

2　These are the facts as we have received them:
　　Christ has fulfilled what the Scriptures foretold,
　　Adam's whole family in death had been sleeping,
　　Christ through His rising restores us to life.

3　These are the facts as we have received them:
　　we, with our Saviour, have died on the cross;
　　now, having risen, our Jesus lives in us,
　　gives us His Spirit and makes us His home.

4　These are the facts as we have received them:
　　we shall be changed in the blink of an eye,
　　trumpets shall sound as we face life immortal,
　　this is the victory through Jesus our Lord.

5　These are the facts as we have received them,
　　these are the truths that the Christian believes,
　　this is the basis of all of our preaching:
　　Christ died for sinners and rose from the tomb.

688   They that wait upon the Lord

Words and music: Andy Silver

They that wait up-on the Lord shall re-new their strength, and mount on ea-gles wings. They that wait up-on the Lord shall re-new their strength, and mount on ea-gles wings.

689

Thine be the glory

MACCABAEUS   10 11 11 11 with refrain

Words: Edmond Budry (1854–1932)
tr. R Birch Hoyle (1875–1939)
Music: G F Handel (1685–1759)

Thine be the glo - ry, ri - sen,— con-quering Son,

end - less— is the vic - tory Thou o'er death hast won;

an - gels— in bright rai - ment rolled the stone a - way,

kept the— fold - ed grave-clothes where Thy bo - dy lay.

Thine be the glo-ry, ri-sen,__ con-quering Son,

end-less__ is the vic-tory Thou o'er death hast won.

1   Thine be the glory, risen, conquering Son,
      endless is the victory Thou o'er death hast won;
      angels in bright raiment rolled the stone away,
      kept the folded grave-clothes where Thy body lay.
          Thine be the glory, risen, conquering Son,
          endless is the victory Thou o'er death hast won.

2   Lo! Jesus meets us, risen from the tomb;
      lovingly He greets us, scatters fear and gloom;
      let the Church with gladness hymns of triumph sing,
      for her Lord now liveth; death hath lost its sting.
          Thine be the glory . . .

3   No more we doubt Thee, glorious Prince of life;
      life is nought without Thee: aid us in our strife;
      make us more than conquerors, through Thy deathless love:
      bring us safe through Jordan to Thy home above.
          Thine be the glory . . .

690 This Child

Words and music: Graham Kendrick
Music arranged Christopher Norton

This Child, se-cret-ly comes in the night, oh, this Child, hid-ing a hea-ven-ly light, oh, this Child, com-ing to us like a stran-ger, this hea-ven-ly Child. *This* Child, hea-ven come down now to be with us here, hea-ven-ly love

_____ and mer - cy ap - pear, soft-ly in awe _____ and won - der come

near to this hea - ven-ly Child. This

3. Child. **D.%** **4.** This Child.

1 This Child, secretly comes in the night,
   oh, this Child, hiding a heavenly light,
   oh, this Child, coming to us like a stranger,
   this heavenly Child.

   This Child, heaven come down now to be with us here,
   heavenly love and mercy appear,
   softly in awe and wonder come near
   to this heavenly Child.

2 This Child, rising on us like the sun,
   oh this Child, given to light everyone,
   oh this Child, guiding our feet on the pathway
   to peace on earth.

   This Child, heaven come down . . .

3 This Child, raising the humble and poor,
   oh this Child, making the proud ones to fall;
   this Child, filling the hungry with good things,
   this heavenly Child.

   This Child, heaven come down . . .

691   This is the day

Words: Les Garrett
Music: Fiji Island folk melody
Music arranged Roland Fudge

1 This is the day,   this is the day   that the
2 This is the day,   this is the day   when He
3 This is the day,   this is the day   when the

Lord has made, that the Lord has made.
rose a - gain, when He rose a - gain.
Spi - rit came, when the Spi - rit came.

We will re - joice,   we will re - joice and be

glad in it, and be glad in it.

692   This is what our Saviour said

Words and music: Greg Leavers
and Phil Burt

This is what our Sav-iour said, He will re-turn to the

earth in pow-er, com-ing on the clouds from heaven,

all earth shall see Him and bow be-fore Him. He is the Al-pha and O-me-ga,

Who is, and who was, and who is to come;_ once He was dead and be -

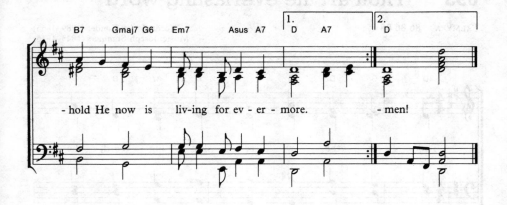

- hold He now is liv-ing for ev - er - more. - men!

1 This is what our Saviour said,
   He will return to the earth in power,
   coming on the clouds from heaven,
   all earth shall see Him and bow before Him.
   He is the Alpha and Omega,
   Who is, and who was, and who is to come;
   once He was dead and behold He now is
   living for evermore.

2 With a shout and trumpet sound
   He'll fetch His bride for the marriage feast,
   and then we'll see Him face to face,
   joining all heaven in praise and worship.
   Blessing and glory and thanksgiving
   be to the Lamb reigning now and forever;
   honour and power belong to Jesus,
   come quickly Lord, amen!

693   Thou art the everlasting word

PALMYRA   86 86 88

Words: Josiah Conder (1789–1855)
Music: Joseph Summers (1843–1916)

Thou art the ev - er - last - ing Word, the
Fa - ther's on - ly Son; God ma - ni - fest - ly
seen and heard, and Heaven's be - lov - èd One: *Wor-thy, O Lamb of*
God, art Thou that ev - ery knee to Thee should bow.

1 Thou art the everlasting Word,
the Father's only Son;
God manifestly seen and heard,
and Heaven's belovèd One:
Worthy, O Lamb of God, art Thou
that every knee to Thee should bow.

2 In Thee most perfectly expressed
the Father's glories shine;
of the full Deity possessed,
eternally divine:
Worthy, O Lamb of God . . .

3 True image of the infinite,
whose essence is concealed;
brightness of uncreated light;
the heart of God revealed:
Worthy, O Lamb of God . . .

4 But the high mysteries of Thy name
an angel's grasp transcend;
the Father only – glorious claim!
the Son can comprehend:
Worthy, O Lamb of God . . .

5 Throughout the universe of bliss,
the centre Thou, and sun;
the eternal theme of praise is this,
to heaven's belovèd One:
Worthy, O Lamb of God . . .

694 Thou art my God

Words and music: Tony Hopkins
Music arranged Roland Fudge

Rich and broad

Thou art my God and I will praise Thee;

Thou art my God, I will ex-alt Thee. O give

thanks un-to the Lord, for He is good; for His

mer-cy en-dur-eth for ev - er.

695 Thou art the Way

St James   CM

Words: George Washington Doane (1799–1859)
Music: Raphael Courteville (1675–1735)

Thou art the way: to Thee a - lone from

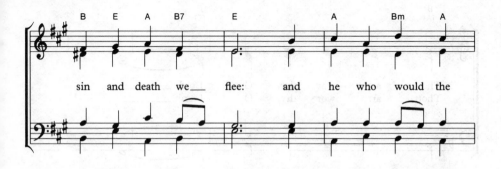

sin and death we___ flee: and he who would the

Fa - ther seek, must seek Him, Lord, by Thee.

1 Thou art the way: to Thee alone
   from sin and death we flee:
   and he who would the Father seek,
   must seek Him, Lord, by Thee.

2 Thou art the truth: Thy word alone
   true wisdom can impart;
   Thou only canst inform the mind
   and purify the heart.

3 Thou art the life: the rending tomb
   proclaims Thy conquering arm;
   and those who put their trust in Thee
   nor death nor hell shall harm.

4 Thou art the way, the truth, the life;
   grant us that way to know,
   that truth to keep, that life to win,
   whose joys eternal flow.

696 Thou art worthy

Words and music: Pauline Michael Mills
verse 2 by Tom Smail

1 Thou art wor-thy, Thou art wor-thy,
2 Thou art wor-thy, Thou art wor-thy,

Thou art wor-thy, O Lord.
Thou art wor-thy, O Lamb.

Thou art wor-thy, to re-ceive glo-ry,
Thou art wor-thy, to re-ceive glo-ry and

glo-ry and hon-our and power. For
power at the Fa-ther's right hand. For

697   Thou didst leave Thy throne

MARGARET   Irregular

Words: Emily Elizabeth Steele Elliott (1836–97)
Music: T R Matthews (1826–1910)

Thou didst leave Thy throne and Thy king-ly crown, when Thou cam-est to earth for me; but in Beth-le-hem's home was there found no room for Thy ho-ly na-ti-vi-ty: O come to my heart, Lord Je-sus, there is room in my heart for Thee.

1 Thou didst leave Thy throne
  and Thy kingly crown,
  when Thou camest to earth for me;
  but in Bethlehem's home
  was there found no room
  for Thy holy nativity:
  O come to my heart, Lord Jesus,
  there is room in my heart for Thee.

2 Heaven's arches rang
  when the angels sang,
  proclaiming Thy royal degree;
  but of lowly birth
  cam'st Thou, Lord, on earth,
  and in great humility:
  O come to my heart, Lord Jesus,
  there is room in my heart for Thee.

3 The foxes found rest,
  and the birds their nest,
  in the shade of the cedar-tree;
  but Thy couch was the sod,
  O Thou Son of God,
  in the deserts of Galilee;
  O come to my heart, Lord Jesus,
  there is room in my heart for Thee.

4 Thou camest, O Lord,
  with the living word
  that should set Thy people free;
  but, with mocking scorn,
  and with crown of thorn,
  they bore Thee to Calvary:
  O come to my heart, Lord Jesus,
  Thy cross is my only plea.

5 When heaven's arches ring,
  and her choirs shall sing,
  at Thy coming to victory,
  let Thy voice call me home,
  saying, 'Yet there is room,
  there is room at my side for thee!'
  And my heart shall rejoice, Lord Jesus,
  when Thou comest and callest for me.

Thou, Lord, hast given Thyself

SPRINGFIELD   11 10 11 10

Words: R D Browne
Music: H J Gauntlett (1805–76)

1 Thou, Lord, hast giv - en Thy - self for our heal - ing;
poured out Thy life that our souls might be freed. Love, from the heart of the
Fa - ther, re - veal - ing light for our dark - ness and grace for our need.

2 Sav - iour of men, our hu - ma - ni - ty shar - ing,
give us a pas - sion for souls that are lost. Help us to fol - low, Thy
gos - pel de - clar - ing; dai - ly to serve Thee and count not the cost.

3 Pray we for men who to - day in their blind - ness
wan - der from Thee and Thy king - dom of truth: grant them a sight of Thy
great lov - ing - kind - ness, Lord of their man - hood and guide of their youth.

4 Come, Holy Spirit, to cleanse and renew us:
purge us from evil and fill us with power:
thus shall the waters of healing flow through us;
so shall revival be born in this hour.

5 Give to Thy Church, as she tells forth the story,
strength for her weakness and trust for her fears;
make her a channel of grace for Thy glory,
answer her prayers in the midst of the years.

699 Thou, whose almighty word

Moscow 664 66 64

Words: John Marriott (1780–1825)
Music: Felice de Giardini (1716–96)

Thou, whose al - migh - ty word cha - os and dark - ness heard, and took their flight;— hear us, we hum - bly pray, and where the Gos - pel day sheds not its glo - rious ray, let there be light!

1 Thou, whose almighty word
chaos and darkness heard,
and took their flight;
hear us, we humbly pray,
and where the Gospel day
sheds not its glorious ray,
let there be light!

2 Thou, who didst come to bring,
on Thy redeeming wing,
healing and sight;
health to the sick in mind,
sight to the inly blind,
O now to all mankind
let there be light!

3 Spirit of truth and love,
Life-giving, holy Dove,
speed forth Thy flight;
move on the water's face,
bearing the lamp of grace,
and in earth's darkest place
let there be light!

4 Blessèd and holy Three,
glorious Trinity,
wisdom, love, might;
boundless as ocean's tide,
rolling in fullest pride,
through the earth, far and wide
let there be light!

700 Thou who wast rich

FRAGRANCE 98 98 98

Words: Frank Houghton
Music: French Carol melody
arranged C H Kitson

Thou who wast rich beyond all splen-dour, all for love's
sake be-cam-est poor, thrones for a man-ger
didst sur-ren-der sap-phire-paved courts for sta-ble
floor. Thou who wast rich be-yond all

splen - dour, all for love's sake___ be - cam - est poor.

1 Thou who wast rich beyond all splendour,
all for love's sake becamest poor,
thrones for a manger didst surrender
sapphire-paved courts for stable floor.
Thou who wast rich beyond all splendour,
all for love's sake becamest poor.

2 Thou who art God beyond all praising,
all for love's sake becamest man;
stooping so low, but sinners raising
heavenwards by Thine eternal plan.
Thou who art God beyond all praising,
all for love's sake becamest man.

3 Thou who art love beyond all telling,
Saviour and King, we worship Thee.
Immanuel, within us dwelling,
make us what Thou wouldst have us be.
Thou who art love beyond all telling,
Saviour and King, we worship Thee.

701 Thou will keep him in perfect peace

Words: Anon
Music: Robert Witty
arranged Paul Beckwith

1 Thou will keep him in perfect peace, (*3 times*)
   whose mind is stayed on Thee.

2 Marvel not that I say unto you, (*3 times*)
   ye must be born again.

3 Though your sins as scarlet be, (*3 times*)
   they shall be white as snow.

4 If the Son shall make you free, (*3 times*)
   ye shall be free indeed.

5 They that wait upon the Lord, (*3 times*)
   they shall renew their strength.

6 Whom shall I send and who will go? (*3 times*)
   Here I am Lord, send me.

702 Through all the changing scenes

WILTSHIRE CM

Words: Nahum Tate (1652–1715)
and Nicholas Brady (1639–1726)
Music: G T Smart (1776–1867)

1 Through all the changing scenes of life,
  in trouble and in joy,
  the praises of my God shall still
  my heart and tongue employ.

2 Of His deliverance I will boast,
  till all that are distressed
  from my example comfort take,
  and charm their griefs to rest.

3 O magnify the Lord with me,
  with me exalt His name;
  when in distress to Him I called,
  He to my rescue came.

4 The hosts of God encamp around
  the dwellings of the just;
  deliverance He affords to all
  who on His succour trust.

5 O make but trial of His love;
  experience will decide
  how blest they are, and only they,
  who in His truth confide.

6 Fear Him, ye saints, and you will then
  have nothing else to fear;
  make you His service your delight,
  He'll make your wants His care.

703 Through our God

Words and music: Dale Garratt
Music arranged Christopher Norton

Resolutely

Through our God we shall do val - iant - ly, it is He who will tread down our e - ne - mies; we'll sing and shout His vic - to - ry: Christ is King! For God has won the vic - to - ry and

3rd time **to Coda** ⊕

set_____ His peo-ple free; His word_____ has slain the

e - ne - my,_ the earth shall stand and see that – through our

⊕ *CODA*

Christ is King,

Christ is King, Christ is King!

704 Through the love of our God

SOUTHGATE 84 84 88 84

Words: Mary Peters (1813–56)
Music: Thomas B Southgate (1814–68)

Through the love of God our Sav-iour all will be well;

free and change-less is His fa-vour, all,— all is well.

Pre-cious is the blood that heals us, per - fect_ is the grace that seals us,

strong the hand stretched out to shield us; all_____ must be well.

1 Through the love of God our Saviour
    all will be well;
free and changeless is His favour,
    all, all is well.
Precious is the blood that heals us,
perfect is the grace that seals us,
strong the hand stretched out to shield us;
    all must be well.

2 Though we pass through tribulation,
    all will be well;
ours is such a full salvation,
    all, all is well.
Happy, still in God confiding;
fruitful, if in Christ abiding;
holy, through the Spirit's guiding;
    all must be well.

3 We expect a bright tomorrow;
    all will be well;
faith can sing, through days of sorrow
    'All, all is well.'
On our Father's love relying,
Jesus every need supplying,
or in living or in dying,
    all must be well.

705 Thy hand, O God, has guided

THORNBURY 76 76 D

Words: E H Plumptre (1821–91)
Music: Basil Harwood (1859–1949)

Thy hand, O God, has guid - ed Thy flock, from age____ to age;_____ the won-drous tale is writ - ten, full clear on ev - ery page;_____ our fa - thers owned Thy____ good - ness, and we____ their deeds re -

1   Thy hand, O God, has guided
    Thy flock, from age to age;
    the wondrous tale is written,
    full clear on every page;
    our fathers owned Thy goodness,
    and we their deeds record;
    and both of this bear witness:
    One Church, one Faith, one Lord.

2   Thy heralds brought glad tidings
    to greatest as to least;
    they bade men rise and hasten
    to share the great King's feast;
    and this was all their teaching
    in every deed and word;
    to all alike proclaiming:
    One Church, one Faith, one Lord.

3   Through many a day of darkness,
    through many a scene of strife,
    the faithful few fought bravely
    to guard the nation's life.
    Their gospel of redemption,
    sin pardoned, man restored,
    was all in this enfolded:
    One Church, one Faith, one Lord.

4   Thy mercy will not fail us,
    nor leave Thy work undone;
    with Thy right hand to help us,
    the victory shall be won;
    and then, by men and angels,
    Thy name shall be adored,
    and this shall be their anthem:
    One Church, one Faith, one Lord.

Thy loving-kindness

Words and music: Hugh Mitchell
Music arranged Roger Mayor

2 I lift my hands up unto Thy name,
   I lift my hands up unto Thy name;
   my lips shall praise Thee, thus will I bless Thee;
   Thy loving-kindness is better than life.

707 Timeless love!

Words: Timothy Dudley-Smith
Music: Norman Warren

708   To God be the glory!

Words: Frances van Alstyne (1820–1915)
(Fanny J Crosby)
Music: W H Doane (1832–1916)

To God＿ be the glo - ry! great things He hath done; so

loved He the world that He gave us His＿ Son; who yield - ed His

life an a - tone - ment for sin, and o - pened the

life gate that all may go in. *Praise the Lord, praise the Lord! let the*

earth hear His voice; praise the Lord, praise the Lord! let the peo-ple re-joice: O come to the Fa-ther, through Je-sus the Son and give Him the glo-ry; great things He hath done!

1 To God be the glory! great things He hath done;
so loved He the world that He gave us His Son;
who yielded His life an atonement for sin,
and opened the life gate that all may go in.
    Praise the Lord, praise the Lord!
    let the earth hear His voice;
    praise the Lord, praise the Lord!
    let the people rejoice:
    O come to the Father,
    through Jesus the Son
    and give Him the glory;
    great things He hath done!

2 O perfect redemption, the purchase of blood!
to every believer the promise of God;
the vilest offender who truly believes,
that moment from Jesus a pardon receives.
    Praise the Lord . . .

3 Great things He hath taught us, great things He hath done,
and great our rejoicing through Jesus the Son;
but purer, and higher, and greater will be
our wonder, our rapture, when Jesus we see.
    Praise the Lord . . .

709 To Him we come

LIVING LORD   98 88 83

Words: James E Seddon (1915–83)
Music: Patrick Appleford

To Him we come — Je - sus Christ our Lord,
God's own liv - ing Word, His dear Son: _____
in Him there is ___ no east and west, in Him all na - tions shall be blessed;
to all He of - fers peace and rest – lov - ing ___ Lord!

1 To Him we come –
Jesus Christ our Lord,
God's own living Word,
His dear Son:
in Him there is no east and west,
in Him all nations shall be blessed;
to all He offers peace and rest –
    loving Lord!

2 In Him we live –
Christ our strength and stay,
life and truth and way,
friend divine:
His power can break the chains of sin,
still all life's storms without, within,
help us the daily fight to win –
    living Lord!

3 For Him we go –
soldiers of the cross,
counting all things loss
Him to know;
going to every land and race,
preaching to all redeeming grace,
building His church in every place –
    conquering Lord!

4 With Him we serve –
His the work we share
with saints everywhere,
near and far;
one in the task which faith requires,
one in the zeal which never tires,
one in the hope His love inspires –
    coming Lord!

5 Onward we go –
faithful, bold, and true,
called His will to do
day by day
till, at the last, with joy we'll see
Jesus, in glorious majesty;
live with Him through eternity –
    reigning Lord!

710   To Him who is able to keep us

Words and music: Andy Silver

In Hebrew style

To Him who is a - ble to keep us, to
keep us from fall - ing a - way, who'll
bring us, spot - less and joy - ful, in - to God's
pre - sence one day. To the on - ly God

our Sav - iour, through Je - sus Christ _ our
Lord be glo - ry, ma - jes - ty, might and
pow - er, now, al - ways _ a - men.

To Him who is able to keep us,
to keep us from falling away,
who'll bring us, spotless and joyful,
into God's presence one day.
To the only God our Saviour,
through Jesus Christ our Lord
be glory, majesty, might and power,
now, always – amen.

711 True-hearted, whole-hearted

True-Hearted 11 10 11 10

Words: Frances Ridley Havergal (1836–79)
altered Horrobin/Leavers
Music: Josiah Booth (1852–1930)

True-heart-ed, whole-heart-ed, faith-ful and loy-al,

King of our lives, by Your grace we'll stay true! Un-der Your stand-ard, ex-

-alt-ed and roy-al, strong in Your strength, we will bat-tle for You!

Peal out the watch-word, and si-lence it ne-ver,

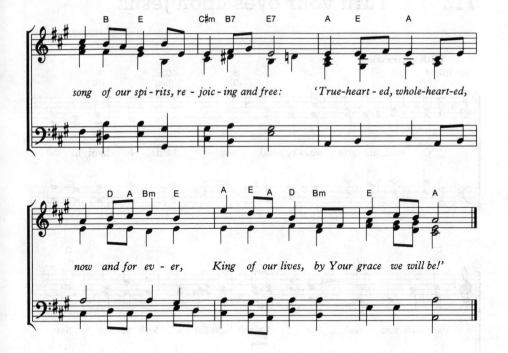

song of our spi-rits, re-joic-ing and free: 'True-heart-ed, whole-heart-ed,

now and for ev-er, King of our lives, by Your grace we will be!'

1 True-hearted, whole-hearted, faithful and loyal,
King of our lives, by Your grace we'll stay true!
Under Your standard, exalted and royal,
strong in Your strength, we will battle for You!
Peal out the watchword, and silence it never,
song of our spirits, rejoicing and free:
'True-hearted, whole-hearted, now and for ever,
King of our lives, by Your grace we will be!'

2 True-hearted, whole-hearted! fullest allegiance
yielding each day to our glorious King!
Valiant endeavour and loving obedience
freely and joyously now would we bring.
Peal out the watchword . . .

3 True-hearted! Saviour, You know all our story,
weak are the hearts that we lay at Your feet;
sinful and treacherous, yet, for Your glory,
heal them and cleanse them from sin and deceit.
Peal out the watchword . . .

4 True-hearted, whole-hearted! Saviour, all-glorious,
take Your great power and You reign alone,
over our wills and affections victorious –
freely surrendered and wholly Your own.
Peal out the watchword . . .

712

Turn your eyes upon Jesus

Words and music: Helen H Lemmel

O soul, are you wea-ry and trou - bled? No light in the
dark-ness you see?_____ There's light for a look at the Sav -
-iour, and life more a - bun-dant and free!

Turn your eyes up-on Je - sus, look full in His

won - der - ful face;_____ and the things of earth will grow

strange - ly dim in the light of His glo - ry and grace._____

1 O soul, are you weary and troubled?
No light in the darkness you see?
There's light for a look at the Saviour,
and life more abundant and free!
  Turn your eyes upon Jesus,
  look full in His wonderful face;
  and the things of earth will grow strangely dim
  in the light of His glory and grace.

2 Through death into life everlasting
He passed and we follow Him there;
over us sin no more hath dominion,
for more than conquerors we are!
  Turn your eyes . . .

3 His word shall not fail you He promised;
believe Him, and all will be well:
then go to a world that is dying,
His perfect salvation to tell.
  Turn your eyes . . .

713 Tonight

Words and music: Graham Kendrick
Music arranged Christopher Norton

to find___ it was_ all

true;　　　　　　　　　　des - pised___　and worth-less

shep - herds,_____　　　　we were___　the first_ to

know!_____

714   Unto us a Boy is born!

PUER NOBIS   76 77

Words: German (15th century)
tr. Percy Dearmer (1867–1936)
Music: German carol melody
arranged Geoffrey Shaw (1879–1943)

1   Unto us a boy is born!
King of all creation,
came He to a world forlorn,
   the Lord of every nation,
   the Lord of every nation.

2   Cradled in a stall was He
with sleepy cows and asses;
but the very beasts could see
   that He all men surpasses,
   that He all men surpasses.

3   Herod then with fear was filled:
'A Prince,' he said, 'in Jewry!'
All the little boys he killed
   at Bethlehem in his fury,
   at Bethlehem in his fury.

4   Now may Mary's Son, who came
so long ago to love us,
lead us all with hearts aflame
   unto the joys above us,
   unto the joys above us.

5   Alpha and Omega He!
Let the organ thunder,
while the choir with peals of glee
   doth rend the air asunder,
   doth rend the air asunder!

715   Victory is on our lips

Words and music: Diane Fung
Music arranged Roland Fudge

716 We are a chosen people

Words and music: David J Hadden

Triumphantly

We are a cho - - sen peo - ple, a
roy - al priest - hood, a ho - ly
na - tion be - long - ing to God. We are a God.
You have called us out of dark - ness

We are a chosen people,
a royal priesthood,
a holy nation belonging to God.

1   You have called us out of darkness
     to declare Your praise;
     we exalt You and enthrone You,
     glorify Your name.
       We are a chosen people . . .

2   You have placed us into Zion,
     in the new Jerusalem;
     thousand thousand are their voices,
     singing to the Lamb.
       We are a chosen people . . .

717

We are here to praise You

Words and music: Graham Kendrick
Music arranged David Peacock

Worshipfully

We are here to praise You,_____ lift our hearts and

sing;_____ we are here to give You_____

the best that we can bring._____ And it is our

love_____ ris-ing from our hearts –_____
give You_____ plea-sure and de-light –_____

ev - ery - thing with - in us cries:_____
heart and mind and will that say:_____

'Ab - ba Fa - ther!'_____ Help us now to

'I love You, Lord.'_____

We are here to praise You,
lift our hearts and sing;
we are here to give You
the best that we can bring.
And it is our love
rising from our hearts –
everything within us cries:
'Abba Father!'
Help us now to give You
pleasure and delight –
heart and mind and will that say:
'I love You, Lord.'

718   We are marching

Words and music: Graham Kendrick
Music arranged Christopher Norton

We are march-ing in the great pro - ces - sion, sing-ers and dan - cers, and mu - si - cians; with the great con-gre - ga - tion we are mov-ing on - ward, ev-er fur-ther and deep - er_____ in - to the heart of____ God.

O give thanks to the Lord, for His

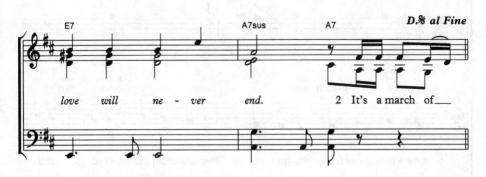

D.𝄋 al Fine

love will ne - ver end. 2 It's a march of___

1 We are marching
  in the great procession,
  singers and dancers,
  and musicians;
  with the great congregation
  we are moving onward,
  ever further and deeper
  into the heart of God.
    O give thanks to the Lord,
    for His love will never end.

2 It's a march of victory,
  it's a march of triumph,
  lifting Jesus higher
  on a throne of praise.
  With the banner of love
  flying over us,
  ever further and deeper
  into the heart of God.
    O give thanks . . .

3 We will go to the nations,
  spreading wide the fragrance
  of the knowledge of Jesus
  into every place.
  Hear the great cloud of witnesses
  cheer us onward,
  ever further and deeper
  into the heart of God.
    O give thanks . . .

4 And the whole creation
  waits in expectation
  of the full revelation
  of the sons of God;
  as we march through history
  to our blood-bought destiny,
  ever further and deeper
  into the heart of God.

  Ever further and deeper
  into the heart of God.

719

We are moving on

Words and music: Ian Traynar
Music arranged Christopher Norton

We are mov-ing on in-to a deep ap-pre-ci-a-tion of the

love which flows from Fa-ther out to ev-ery child of God; of the

grace with which He han-dles ev-ery min-ute si-tu-a-tion, how He

wants the best for ev-ery-one who gives to Him his all.

Grace it seems is all He has, and one big o-pen heart; and it's
so good be-ing loved by You, my Lord.

1 We are moving on into
  a deep appreciation
  of the love which flows from Father out
  to every child of God;
  of the grace with which He handles
  every minute situation,
  how He wants the best for everyone
  who gives to Him his all.
    Grace it seems is all He has,
    and one big open heart;
    and it's so good
    being loved by You, my Lord.

2 We will know and understand
  His purposes more clearly,
  O the mystery of the things He does
  in making us more whole.
  With His love He woos us,
  by His grace He sets us free;
  we can only trust Him
  and just hold on to His hand.
    Grace it seems . . .

720 We believe

Words and music: Graham Kendrick
Music arranged Roger Mayor

1 We be-lieve in God the Fa-ther, ma-ker of the u-ni-verse, and in Christ His Son our sav-iour, come to us by vir-gin birth. We be-lieve He died to save us, bore our sins, was cru-ci-fied; then from death He rose vic-to-rious, a-scen-ded to the Fa-ther's side.

2 We be-lieve He sends His Spi-rit on His church with gifts of power; God, His word of truth af-firm-ing, sends us to the na-tions now. He will come a-gain in glo-ry, judge the liv-ing and the dead: ev-ery knee shall bow be-fore Him, then must ev-ery tongue con-fess.

8va

721   We break this bread

Words: from *The Alternative Service Book 1980*
Music: Chris Rolinson
Music arranged Christopher Norton

we are one bo-dy,_____ be-cause we all_ share, we

1.
all share in one bread._____ Though we are

2.
all share in one bread._____

1 MEN   We break this bread
          to share in the body of Christ:
   WOMEN we break this bread
          to share in the body of Christ:
   ALL   though we are many,
          we are one body,
          because we all share,
          we all share in one bread.

2 MEN   We drink this cup
          to share in the body of Christ:
   WOMEN we drink this cup
          to share in the body of Christ:
   ALL   though we are many,
          we are one body,
          because we all share,
          we all share in one cup.

722   We bring the sacrifice of praise

Words and music: Kirk Dearman

We bring the sacrifice of praise
into the house of the Lord;
we bring the sacrifice of praise
into the house of the Lord;
and we offer up to You
the sacrifices of thanksgiving;
and we offer up to You
the sacrifices of joy.

723   We come as guests invited

PASSION CHORALE   76 76 D

Words: Timothy Dudley-Smith
Music: Hans Hassler (1564–1612)
arranged J S Bach (1685–1750)

We come as guests in-vi-ted when Je-sus bids us dine, His friends on earth u-ni-ted to share the bread and wine; the bread of life is bro-ken, the wine is free-ly poured for

us,_ in_ so - lemn to - ken of_ Christ our dy - ing_ Lord.

1   We come as guests invited
    when Jesus bids us dine,
    His friends on earth united
    to share the bread and wine;
    the bread of life is broken,
    the wine is freely poured
    for us, in solemn token
    of Christ our dying Lord.

2   We eat and drink, receiving
    from Christ the grace we need,
    and in our hearts believing
    on Him by faith we feed;
    with wonder and thanksgiving
    for love that knows no end,
    we find in Jesus living
    our ever-present friend.

3   One bread is ours for sharing,
    one single fruitful vine,
    our fellowship declaring
    renewed in bread and wine –
    renewed, sustained and given
    by token, sign and word,
    the pledge and seal of heaven,
    the love of Christ our Lord.

724   We come unto our father's God

THE GOLDEN CHAIN   87 87 887

Words: Thomas Hornblower Gill (1819–1906)
Music: Joseph Barnby (1838–96)

We come un-to our fa-ther's God: their

rock is our sal-va-tion: the e-ter-nal arms, their

dear a-bode, we make our__ ha-bi-ta-tion: we

bring Thee, Lord, the praise they brought; we seek Thee as Thy

saints have sought in ___ ev - ery ge - ne - ra - tion.

1 We come unto our father's God:
    their rock is our salvation:
    the eternal arms, their dear abode,
    we make our habitation:
    we bring Thee, Lord, the praise they brought;
    we seek Thee as Thy saints have sought
    in every generation.

2 The fire divine, their steps that led,
    still goeth bright before us;
    the heavenly shield, around them spread,
    is still high holden o'er us;
    the grace those sinners that subdued,
    the strength those weaklings that renewed,
    doth vanquish, doth restore us.

3 The cleaving sins that brought them low
    are still our souls oppressing;
    the tears that from their eyes did flow
    fall fast, our shame confessing;
    as with Thee, Lord, prevailed their cry,
    so now our prayer ascends on high,
    and bringeth down Thy blessing.

4 Their joy unto their Lord we bring;
    their song to us descendeth:
    the Spirit who in them did sing
    to us His music lendeth.
    His song in them, in us, is one;
    we raise it high, we send it on –
    the song that never endeth!

5 Ye saints to come, take up the strain,
    the same sweet theme endeavour!
    Unbroken be the golden chain,
    keep on the song for ever!
    Safe in the same dear dwelling-place,
    rich with the same eternal grace,
    bless the same boundless giver!

725   We cry, Hosanna, Lord

Words and music: Mimi Farra

Words and music: © 1975 Celebration,
administered in Europe by Thankyou Music,
PO Box 75, Eastbourne, East Sussex BN23 6NW, UK

D.C. al Fine

God! He of - fers___ Him - self, and He
by; should we for - get to praise our___
- ty; His vic - tory o - ver death is the e -

comes a - mong us, a low - ly ser - vant to all.
God, the ve - ry___ stones would sing.
- ter - nal sign of God's love for___ us.

We cry hosanna, Lord;
yes, hosanna, Lord;
yes, hosanna, Lord, to You:
we cry hosanna, Lord;
yes, hosanna, Lord;
yes, hosanna, Lord, to You!

1 Behold, our Saviour comes!
 behold the Son of our God!
 He offers Himself, and He comes among us,
 a lowly servant to all.
  We cry hosanna . . .

2 Children wave their palms
 as the King of all kings rides by;
 should we forget to praise our God,
 the very stones would sing.
  We cry hosanna . . .

3 He comes to set us free,
 He gives us liberty;
 His victory over death is the eternal sign
 of God's love for us.
  We cry hosanna . . .

726   We declare Your majesty

Words and music: Malcolm du Plessis
Music arranged Roger Mayor

We de-clare Your ma-jes-ty, we pro-claim that Your name is ex-alt-ed; for You reign mag-ni-fi-cent-ly, rule vic-to-ri-ous-ly, and Your power is shown through-out the earth. And we ex-

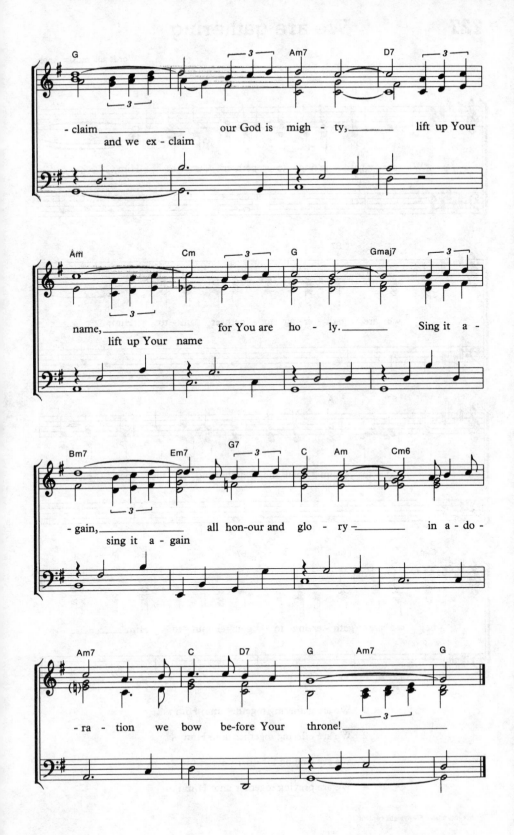

727   We are gathering

Words and music: Anon

1   We are gathering together unto Him . . .

2   We are offering together unto Him . . .

3   We are singing together unto Him . . .

4   We are praying together unto Him . . .

728   We have a gospel to proclaim

FULDA   LM

Words: Edward J Burns
Music: W Gardiner's *Sacred Melodies*, 1815

1   We have a gospel to proclaim,
    good news for men in all the earth;
    the gospel of a saviour's name:
    we sing His glory, tell His worth.

2   Tell of His birth at Bethlehem,
    not in a royal house or hall
    but in a stable dark and dim:
    the Word made flesh, a light for all.

3   Tell of His death at Calvary,
    hated by those He came to save;
    in lonely suffering on the cross
    for all He loved, His life He gave.

4   Tell of that glorious Easter morn:
    empty the tomb, for He was free;
    He broke the power of death and hell
    that we might share His victory.

5   Tell of His reign at God's right hand,
    by all creation glorified;
    He sends His Spirit on His church
    to live for Him, the Lamb who died.

6   Now we rejoice to name Him king:
    Jesus is Lord of all the earth;
    this gospel-message we proclaim:
    we sing His glory, tell His worth.

729   We have come into His house

Lord,   wor - ship Him,   Christ___ the Lord.___

1   We have come into His house,
     and gathered in His name to worship Him.
     We have come into His house,
     and gathered in His name to worship Him.
     We have come into His house,
     and gathered in His name to worship Christ the Lord,
     worship Him, Christ the Lord.

2   So forget about yourself
     and concentrate on Him and worship Him.
     So forget about yourself
     and concentrate on Him and worship Him.
     So forget about yourself
     and concentrate on Him and worship Christ the Lord,
     worship Him, Christ the Lord.

3   Let us lift up holy hands
     and magnify His name and worship Him.
     Let us lift up holy hands
     and magnify His name and worship Him.
     Let us lift up holy hands
     and magnify His name and worship Him,
     worship Him, Christ the Lord.

730   We have heard a joyful sound

LIMPSFIELD   73 73 77 73

Words: Priscilla Owens (1829–1907)
Music: Josiah Booth (1852–1929)

1 We have heard a joy-ful sound: Je - sus saves!
2 Sing a-bove the bat - tle's strife: Je - sus saves!
3 Give the winds a migh - ty voice: Je - sus saves!

Spread the glad-ness all a-round: Je - sus saves!
By His death and end - less life, Je - sus saves!
Let the na-tions now re-joice: Je - sus saves!

Bear the news to ev - ery land, climb the steeps and cross the waves;
Sing it soft-ly through the gloom, when the heart for mer - cy craves;
Shout sal - va-tion full and free to ev - ery strand that o - cean laves –

On - ward! 'tis our Lord's com-mand: Je - sus saves!
sing in tri - umph o'er the tomb: Je - sus saves!
this our song of vic - to - ry: Je - sus saves!

731   We love the place, O God

QUAM DILECTA   66 66

Words: William Bullock (1798–1874)
and H W Baker (1821–77)
Music: Henry Lascelles Jenner (1820–98)

We love the place, O God, where-in Thine hon-our dwells;

the joy of Thine a - bode all earth-ly joy ex - cels.

1   We love the place, O God,
    wherein Thine honour dwells;
    the joy of Thine abode
    all earthly joy excels.

2   It is the house of prayer,
    wherein Thy servants meet;
    and Thou, O Lord, art there,
    Thy chosen flock to greet.

3   We love the word of life,
    the word that tells of peace,
    of comfort in the strife,
    and joys that never cease.

4   We love to sing below
    of mercies freely given;
    but O we long to know
    the triumph-song of heaven.

5   Lord Jesus, give us grace,
    on earth to love Thee more,
    in heaven to see Thy face,
    and with Thy saints adore.

732 We plough the fields

WIR PFLÜGEN 76 76 D with refrain

Words: Matthias Claudius (1740–1815)
tr. Jane Montgomery Campbell (1817–78)
altered Horrobin/Leavers
Music: J A P Schulz (1747–1800)

We plough the fields and scat - ter the good seed on the land,

but it is fed and wa - tered by God's al - migh - ty hand;

He sends the snow in win - ter, the warmth to swell the grain,

the breez - es and the sun - shine and soft re - fresh - ing rain.

All good gifts a-round us are sent from heaven a-bove, then thank the Lord, O thank the Lord, for all His love.

1   We plough the fields and scatter
     the good seed on the land,
     but it is fed and watered
     by God's almighty hand;
     He sends the snow in winter,
     the warmth to swell the grain,
     the breezes and the sunshine
     and soft refreshing rain.
        All good gifts around us
        are sent from heaven above,
        then thank the Lord, O thank the Lord,
        for all His love.

2   He only is the Maker
     of all things near and far;
     He paints the wayside flower,
     He lights the evening star;
     the wind and waves obey Him,
     by Him the birds are fed;
     much more to us, His children,
     He gives our daily bread.
        All good gifts . . .

3   We thank You then, O Father,
     for all things bright and good,
     the seed-time and the harvest,
     our life, our health, our food.
     Accept the gifts we offer
     for all Your love imparts;
     we come now, Lord, to give You
     our humble, thankful hearts.
        All good gifts . . .

733   We praise You, we bless You

St Luke   11 11 11 11

Words: Frances van Alstyne (1820–1915)
(Fanny J Crosby)
altered Horrobin/Leavers
Music: Anon

We praise You, we bless You, our Sav-iour di-vine,
all power and do-min-ion are Yours for all time!
We sing of__ Your mer-cy with joy-ful ac-claim,
for You have re-deemed us: all praise to Your name!

1 We praise You, we bless You, our Saviour divine,
  all power and dominion are Yours for all time!
  We sing of Your mercy with joyful acclaim,
  for You have redeemed us: all praise to Your name!

2 All honour and praise to Your excellent name,
  Your love is unchanging – for ever the same!
  We bless and adore You, O Saviour and King;
  with joy and thanksgiving Your praises we sing!

3 The strength of the hills and the depths of the sea,
  the earth and its fulness, Yours always shall be;
  and yet to the lowly You listen with care,
  so ready their humble petitions to hear.

4 Your infinite goodness our tongues shall employ;
  You give to us richly all things to enjoy;
  we'll follow Your footsteps, we'll rest in Your love,
  and soon we shall praise You in mansions above!

734 We really want to thank You, Lord

Words: Ed Baggett
verse 3 after T Ken (1637–1710)
Music: Ed Baggett
arranged Betty Pulkingham

We real - ly want to thank You, Lord, we real - ly want to

bless Your name: Hal - le - lu - jah! Je - sus is___ our

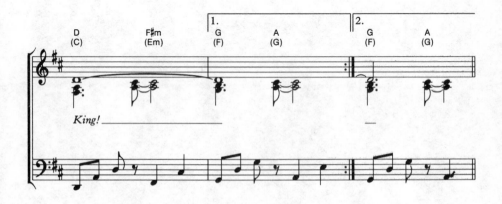

King!___

735   We rest on Thee

FINLANDIA   11 10 11 10 11 10

Words: Edith Gilling Cherry (1872–97)
Music: Jean Sibelius (1865–1957)

We rest on Thee, our shield and our de - fend - er!

we go not forth a - lone a - gainst the foe;

strong in Thy strength, safe in Thy keep - ing ten - der,

we rest on Thee, and in Thy name we go.

Music: © Breitkopf & Härtel, Wiesbaden

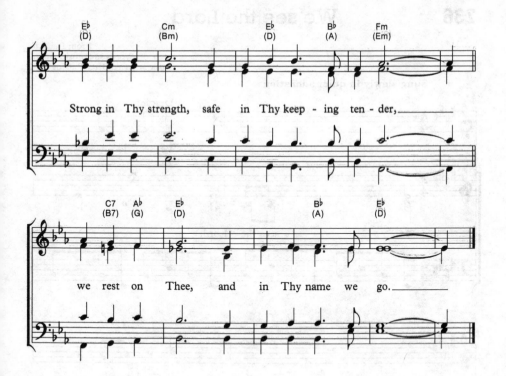

Strong in Thy strength, safe in Thy keep - ing ten - der,_____
we rest on Thee, and in Thy name we go._____

1 We rest on Thee, our shield and our defender!
   we go not forth alone against the foe;
   strong in Thy strength, safe in Thy keeping tender,
   we rest on Thee, and in Thy name we go.
   Strong in Thy strength, safe in Thy keeping tender,
   we rest on Thee, and in Thy name we go.

2 Yes, in Thy name, O Captain of salvation!
   in Thy dear name, all other names above;
   Jesus our righteousness, our sure foundation,
   our Prince of glory and our King of love.
   Jesus our righteousness, our sure foundation,
   our Prince of glory and our King of love.

3 We go in faith, our own great weakness feeling,
   and needing more each day Thy grace to know:
   yet from our hearts a song of triumph pealing,
   'We rest on Thee, and in Thy name we go.'
   Yet from our hearts a song of triumph pealing,
   'We rest on Thee, and in Thy name we go.'

4 We rest on Thee, our shield and our defender!
   Thine is the battle, Thine shall be the praise;
   when passing through the gates of pearly splendour,
   victors, we rest with Thee, through endless days.
   When passing through the gates of pearly splendour,
   victors, we rest with Thee, through endless days.

736

We see the Lord

From Isaiah 6
Words and music: Anon
Music arranged Betty Pulkingham

Sung slowly in quiet adoration

We see Je - sus,

We see the Lord,

we see Je - sus.

we see the Lord, and He is

High,_____ He is high,_____

high and lift - ed up, and His train fills the tem - ple; He is

We shall stand

Words and music: Graham Kendrick
Music arranged Christopher Norton

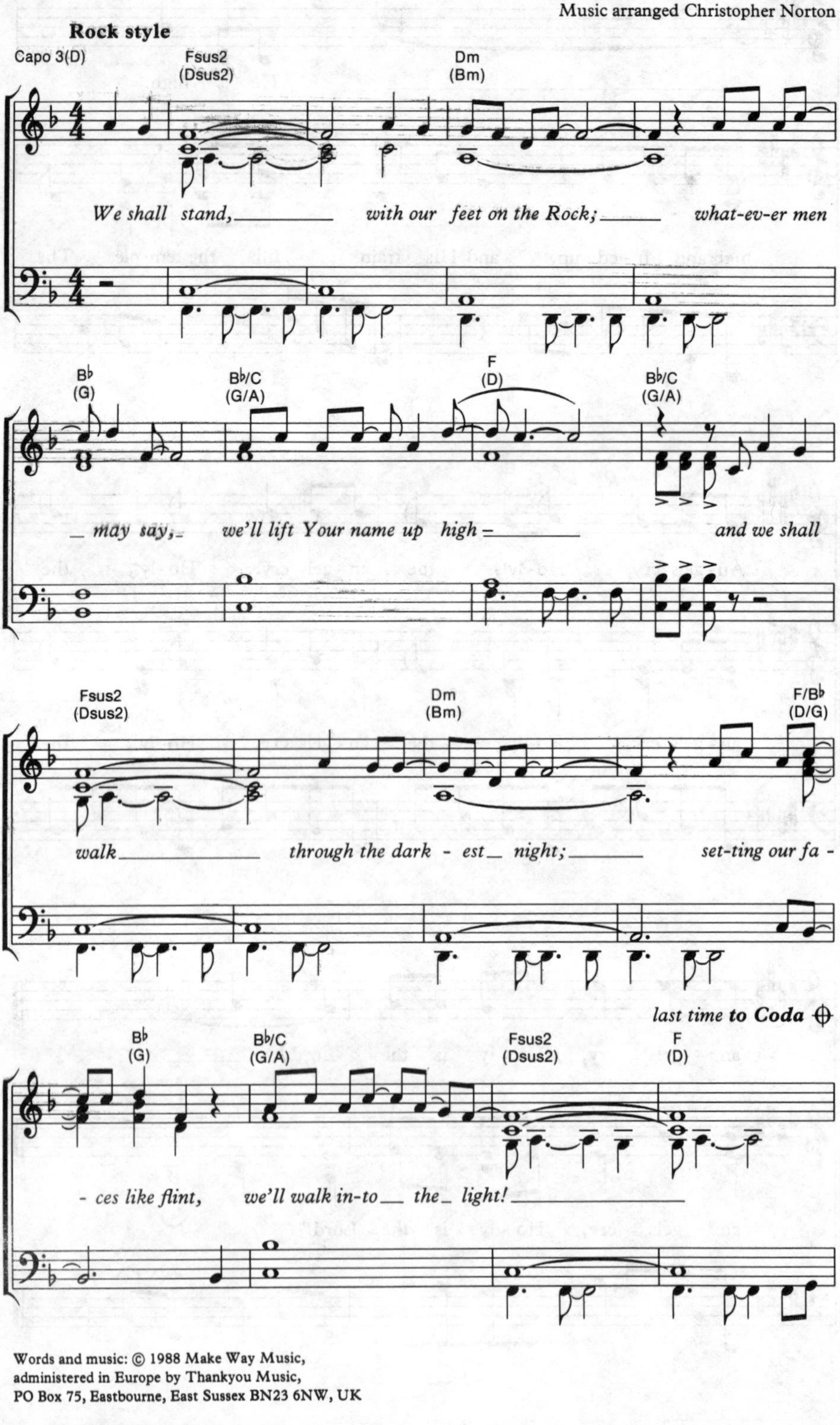

Rock style
Capo 3(D)
Fsus2 (Dsus2)
Dm (Bm)
We shall stand, with our feet on the Rock; what-ev-er men
B♭ (G)
B♭/C (G/A)
F (D)
B♭/C (G/A)
may say, we'll lift Your name up high and we shall
Fsus2 (Dsus2)
Dm (Bm)
F/B♭ (D/G)
walk through the dark - est night; set-ting our fa -
last time to Coda
B♭ (G)
B♭/C (G/A)
Fsus2 (Dsus2)
F (D)
- ces like flint, we'll walk in-to the light!

738
We sing the praise

WARRINGTON LM

Words: Thomas Kelly (1769–1855)
Music: R Harrison (1748–1810)

1 We sing the praise of Him who died,
of Him who died upon the cross;
the sinner's hope let men deride,
for this we count the world but lost.

2 Inscribed upon the cross we see,
in shining letters, 'God is love';
He bears our sins upon the tree,
He brings us mercy from above.

3 The cross! it takes our guilt away,
it holds the fainting spirit up;
it cheers with hope the gloomy day
and sweetens every bitter cup.

4 It makes the coward spirit brave,
and nerves the feeble arm for fight;
it takes the terror from the grave,
and gilds the bed of death with light.

5 The balm of life, the cure of woe,
the measure and the pledge of love;
the sinner's refuge here below,
the angels theme in heaven above.

739   We will sing of our Redeemer

Words and music: Gordon Brattle

740   We three kings of Orient are

Words and music: J H Hopkins (1820–91)
Words altered Horrobin/Leavers

We three kings of Or - i - ent are, bear - ing
gifts we tra - vel a - far, field and foun - tain,
moor and moun - tain, fol - low - ing yon - der star:
O____ star of won - der, star of night, star with

roy - al beau - ty bright, west - ward lead - ing, still pro -

-ceed - ing, guide us to the per - fect light.

1 We three kings of Orient are,
   bearing gifts we travel afar,
   field and fountain, moor and mountain,
   following yonder star:
       O star of wonder, star of night,
       star with royal beauty bright,
       westward leading, still proceeding,
       guide us to the perfect light.

2 Born a King on Bethlehem plain,
   gold I bring to crown Him again:
   King for ever, ceasing never,
   over us all to reign.
       O star of wonder . . .

3 Frankincense for Jesus have I,
   God on earth yet Priest on high;
   prayer and praising all men raising:
   worship is earth's reply.
       O star of wonder . . .

4 Myrrh is mine: its bitter perfume
   tells of His death and Calvary's gloom;
   sorrowing, sighing, bleeding, dying,
   sealed in a stone-cold tomb.
       O star of wonder . . .

5 Glorious now, behold Him arise,
   King, and God, and sacrifice!
   Heaven sings out 'Alleluia',
   'Amen' the earth replies.
       O star of wonder . . .

741 We Your people

Words and music: Adrian Snell

1 We Your peo - ple bow be - fore_ You bro - ken and a -
3 Fa - ther, in this hour of dan - ger we will turn to

- shamed; we have turned on Your cre - a - tion,
You: O for - give us, Lord, for - give us

crushed the life You free - ly_ gave.
and our lives and faith re - new.

2 Lord, have mer - cy on Your child - ren
4 Pour Your Ho - ly Spi - rit on_ us,

1 We Your people bow before You
broken and ashamed;
we have turned on Your creation,
crushed the life You freely gave.

2 Lord, have mercy on Your children
weeping and in fear:
for You are our God and Saviour,
Father in Your love draw near.

3 Father, in this hour of danger
we will turn to You:
O forgive us, Lord, forgive us
and our lives and faith renew.

4 Pour Your Holy Spirit on us,
set our hearts aflame:
all shall see Your power in the nations,
may we bring glory to Your name.

742   We'll sing a new song

Words and music: Diane Fung

Lively

We'll sing a new song of glo-rious tri-umph, for we see the gov-ern-ment of God in our lives; lives. He is

crowned God of the whole world, crowned,

King of cre - a - tion, crowned, rul-ing the na - tions

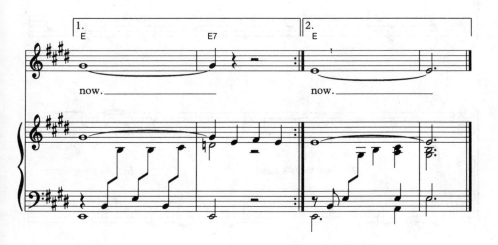

now.   now.

743

We'll walk the land

Words and music: Graham Kendrick
Music arranged Christopher Norton

Rhythmically

Capo 3(D)

1 We'll walk the land with hearts on fire; and ev - ery step will be a prayer. Hope is ris - ing, new day dawn - ing; sound of sing - ing fills the air.

2 Two thou - sand

Let the flame burn

brighter in the heart of the darkness, turning

night to glorious day. Let the song grow louder, as our love grows

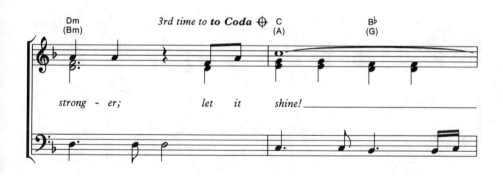

stronger; let it shine!

let it shine!

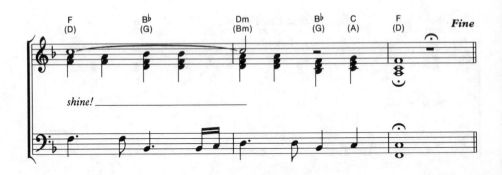

1 We'll walk the land with hearts on fire;
and every step will be a prayer.
Hope is rising, new day dawning;
sound of singing fills the air.

2 Two thousand years, and still the flame
is burning bright across the land.
Hearts are waiting, longing, aching,
for awakening once again.
Let the flame burn brighter
in the heart of the darkness,
turning night to glorious day.
Let the song grow louder,
as our love grows stronger;
let it shine! let it shine!

3 We'll walk for truth, speak out for love;
in Jesus' name we shall be strong,
to lift the fallen, to save the children,
to fill the nation with Your song.
Let the flame . . .

744   We've a story to tell

MESSAGE   10 8 87 with refrain

Words: Colin Sterne (1862–1926)
Music: H E Nichol (1862–1926)

We've a sto-ry to tell to the na - tions, that shall
turn their hearts to the right; a sto-ry of truth and sweet-ness, a
sto-ry of peace and light,____ a sto-ry of peace and light:

For the dark-ness shall turn to dawn - ing, and the

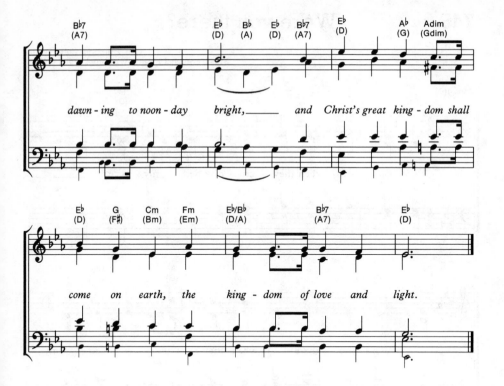

dawn-ing to noon-day bright,___ and Christ's great king-dom shall

come on earth, the king-dom of love and light.

1 We've a story to tell to the nations,
that shall turn their hearts to the right;
a story of truth and sweetness,
a story of peace and light,
a story of peace and light:
For the darkness shall turn to dawning,
and the dawning to noon-day bright,
and Christ's great kingdom shall come on earth,
the kingdom of love and light.

2 We've a song to be sung to the nations,
that shall lift their hearts to the Lord;
a song that shall conquer evil,
and shatter the spear and sword,
and shatter the spear and sword:
For the darkness . . .

3 We've a message to give to the nations,
that the Lord who reigneth above
hath sent us His Son to save us,
and show us that God is love,
and show us that God is love:
For the darkness . . .

4 We've a Saviour to show to the nations,
who the path of sorrow has trod,
that all of the world's great peoples,
might come to the truth of God,
might come to the truth of God:
For the darkness . . .

745   Were you there?

American Folk Hymn
Music arranged Francis Westbrook (1903–1975)

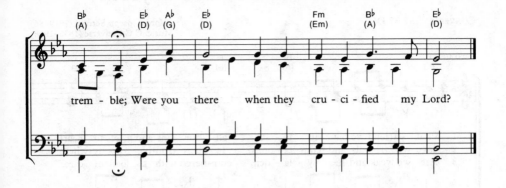

trem - ble; Were you there when they cru - ci - fied my Lord?

1 Were you there when they crucified my Lord?
   Were you there when they crucified my Lord?
   Oh! Sometimes it causes me to tremble, tremble, tremble;
   Were you there when they crucified my Lord?

2 Were you there when they nailed Him to the tree?
   Were you there when they nailed Him to the tree?
   Oh! Sometimes it causes me to tremble, tremble, tremble;
   Were you there when they nailed Him to the tree?

3 Were you there when they laid Him in the tomb?
   Were you there when they laid Him in the tomb?
   Oh! Sometimes it causes me to tremble, tremble, tremble;
   Were you there when they laid Him in the tomb?

4 Were you there when God raised Him from the dead?
   Were you there when God raised Him from the dead?
   Oh! Sometimes it causes me to tremble, tremble, tremble;
   Were you there when God raised Him from the dead?

746   What a friend we have in Jesus

CONVERSE   87 87 D

Words: Joseph Scriven (1819–86)
Music: C C Converse (1832–1918)

1 What a friend we have in Je - sus, all our sins and griefs to bear!
2 Have we tri - als and temp - ta - tions? Is there trou-ble a - ny-where?
3 Are we weak and hea - vy - la - den, cum-bered with a load of care?

What a pri - vi - lege to car - ry ev - ery-thing to God in prayer!
We should ne - ver be dis - cour - aged: take it to the Lord in prayer!
Pre - cious Sav-iour still our re - fuge, take it to the Lord in prayer!

O what peace we of - ten for - feit, O what need-less pain we bear –
Can we find a friend so faith - ful, who will all our sor-rows share?
Do thy friends des-pise, for - sake thee? Take it to the Lord in prayer!

all be-cause we do not car - ry ev - ery-thing to God in prayer!
Je - sus knows our ev - ery weak - ness – take it to the Lord in prayer!
In His arms He'll take and shield thee, thou wilt find a so-lace there.

747   What a mighty God we serve

Words: Unknown
Music: Zulu working song
arranged Phil Burt

With strength and joy

1   What a mighty God we serve . . .
     (*4 times*)

2   He created you and me . . .

3   He has all the power to save . . .

4   Let us praise the living God . . .

5   What a mighty God we serve . . .

748 What a wonderful change

Words: Rufus H McDaniel (1850–1940)
Music: Charles H Gabriel (1856–1932)

What a won-der-ful change in my life has been wrought since
Je-sus came in-to my heart! I have light in my soul for which
long I had sought, since Je-sus came in-to my heart!

Since Je-sus came in-to my heart, since
Since Je-sus came in, came in-to my heart, since

Je-sus came in-to my heart, floods of joy o'er my soul like the
Je-sus came in, came in-to my heart,

sea bil-lows roll, since Je-sus came in-to my heart!

1 What a wonderful change in my life has been wrought
   since Jesus came into my heart!
   I have light in my soul for which long I had sought,
   since Jesus came into my heart!
       Since Jesus came into my heart,
       since Jesus came into my heart,
       floods of joy o'er my soul
       like the sea billows roll,
       since Jesus came into my heart!

2 I have ceased from my wandering and going astray
   since Jesus came into my heart!
   And my sins which were many are all washed away
   since Jesus came into my heart!
       Since Jesus came . . .

3 I'm possessed of a hope that is steadfast and sure,
   since Jesus came into my heart!
   And no dark clouds of doubt now my pathway obscure,
   since Jesus came into my heart!
       Since Jesus came . . .

4 There's a light in the valley of death now for me,
   since Jesus came into my heart!
   And the gates of the city beyond I can see,
   since Jesus came into my heart!
       Since Jesus came . . .

5 I shall go there to dwell in that city, I know,
   since Jesus came into my heart!
   and I'm happy, so happy, as onward I go,
   since Jesus came into my heart!
       Since Jesus came . . .

749   What child is this

GREENSLEEVES   87 87 with refrain

Words: William Chatterton Dix (1837–98)
Music: English traditional melody

What child is this,_ who, laid to rest_ on Ma-ry's lap_ is

sleep - ing? Whom an - gels greet_ with an - thems sweet,_ while

shep - herds watch_ are keep - ing? *This,* *this*___ *is*

Christ *the* *King,_* *whom* *shep - herds* *guard_* *and* *an - gels* *sing:*

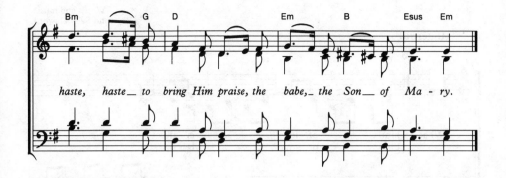

haste, haste to bring Him praise, the babe, the Son of Ma - ry.

1 What child is this, who, laid to rest
on Mary's lap is sleeping?
Whom angels greet with anthems sweet,
while shepherds watch are keeping?
This, this is Christ the King,
whom shepherds guard and angels sing:
haste, haste to bring Him praise,
the babe, the Son of Mary.

2 Why lies He in such mean estate,
where ox and ass are feeding?
Good Christian fear: for sinners here
the silent Word is pleading.
This, this is Christ . . .

3 So bring Him incense, gold, and myrrh,
come, peasant, king, to own Him.
The King of kings salvation brings,
let loving hearts enthrone Him.
This, this is Christ . . .

750   What kind of love is this

Words and music:
Bryn and Sally Haworth

What kind of love __ is this, __
kind of love __ is this? __

that __ gave it - self __ for me?
A __ love I've ne - ver known.

I did - n't e - ven __

I am the __

guil - ty one, yet I

1 What kind of love is this,
   that gave itself for me?
   I am the guilty one,
   yet I go free.
   What kind of love is this?
   A love I've never known.
   I didn't even know His name,
   what kind of love is this?

2 What kind of man is this,
   that died in agony?
   He who had done no wrong
   was crucified for me.
   What kind of man is this,
   who laid aside His throne
   that I may know the love of God?
   What kind of man is this?

3 By grace I have been saved,
   it is the gift of God.
   He destined me to be His son,
   such is His love.
   No eye has ever seen,
   no ear has ever heard,
   nor has the heart of man conceived,
   what kind of love is this?

751 When all Your mercies

CONTEMPLATION   CM

Words: Joseph Addison (1672–1719)
Music: F A Gore Ouseley (1825–89)

1 When all Your mercies, O my God,
    my rising soul surveys,
  transported with the view, I'm lost
    in wonder, love, and praise.

2 Unnumbered comforts on my soul
    Your tender care bestowed,
  before my infant heart conceived
    from whom those comforts flowed.

3 Ten thousand thousand precious gifts
    my daily thanks employ,
  nor is the least a cheerful heart
    that tastes those gifts with joy.

4 Through every period of my life
    Your goodness I'll pursue,
  and after death, in distant worlds,
    the glorious theme renew.

5 Through all eternity to You
    a joyful song I'll raise;
  for O eternity's too short
    to utter all Your praise!

752   When He comes

Words and music: Sue Read
Music arranged Andy Silver
and Christopher Norton

1 When He comes we'll see just a child; no war-rior Lord but a ba-by so mild. The Lord says: 'Beth - le - hem, though you are but small, in___ you shall be born the King.' When He comes, when He comes.___

753   When I feel the touch

Words and music:
Keri Jones and Dave Matthews

Worshipfully

When I feel the touch_____ of Your hand up-on my life,_____ it caus-es me to sing a song, that I love You, Lord. So from deep with -in_____ my spi-rit sing - eth un - to Thee,_____ You are my King, You are my God, and I love You, Lord.

754   When I look into Your holiness

Words and music: Anon
Music arranged Phil Burt

When I look in-to Your ho - li - ness, ____ when I gaze in - to Your love - li - ness, when all things that sur-round be-come sha-dows in the light of You. ____ When I've found the joy ____ of reach - ing Your

When I look into Your holiness,
when I gaze into Your loveliness,
when all things that surround
become shadows in the light of You.

When I've found the joy of reaching Your heart,
when my will becomes enthroned in Your love,
when all things that surround
become shadows in the light of You.

I worship You, I worship You;
the reason I live is to worship You.
I worship You, I worship You;
the reason I live is to worship You.

755 When I survey

ROCKINGHAM LM

Words: Isaac Watts (1674–1748)
Music: E Miller (1731–1807)

1 When I survey the wondrous cross
on which the Prince of glory died,
my richest gain I count but loss,
and pour contempt on all my pride.

2 Forbid it, Lord, that I should boast,
save in the death of Christ my God:
all the vain things that charm me most,
I sacrifice them to His blood.

3 See from His head, His hands, His feet,
sorrow and love flow mingled down:
did e'er such love and sorrow meet,
or thorns compose so rich a crown?

4 Were the whole realm of nature mine,
that were an offering far too small,
love so amazing, so divine,
demands my soul, my life, my all.

756   When morning gilds the skies

LAUDES DOMINI   666 D

Words: tr. from the German by
Edward Caswall (1814–78)
Music: J Barnby (1838–96)

1   When morning gilds the skies,
    my heart awaking cries:
      May Jesus Christ be praised!
    Alike at work and prayer
    to Jesus I repair;
      may Jesus Christ be praised!

2   Does sadness fill my mind?
    a solace here I find –
      may Jesus Christ be praised!
    When evil thoughts molest,
    with this I shield my breast –
      may Jesus Christ be praised!

3   Be this, when day is past,
    of all my thoughts the last:
      May Jesus Christ be praised!
    The night becomes as day,
    when from the heart we say:
      May Jesus Christ be praised!

4   To God, the Word, on high
    the hosts of angels cry:
      May Jesus Christ be praised!
    Let mortals, too, upraise
    their voice in hymns of praise:
      May Jesus Christ be praised!

5   Let earth's wide circle round
    in joyful notes resound:
      May Jesus Christ be praised!
    Let air, and sea, and sky,
    from depth to height, reply:
      May Jesus Christ be praised!

6   Be this while life is mine,
    my canticle divine:
      May Jesus Christ be praised!
    Be this the eternal song
    through all the ages long:
      May Jesus Christ be praised!

757 When peace like a river

Words: Horatio G Spafford (1828–88)
Music: Philip P Bliss
arranged Phil Burt

When peace like a_ ri- ver at-tend- eth my way, when sor- rows like sea- bil- lows roll;_____ what- ev- er my lot You have taught me to say, 'It is_ well, it is

well with my soul.'
(well with my soul)
It is

well, with my soul.'
(it is well) (with my soul)
It is

well, it is well with my soul.

1 When peace like a river attendeth my way,
when sorrows like sea-billows roll;
whatever my lot You have taught me to say,
'It is well, it is well with my soul.'

2 Though Satan should buffet, if trials should come,
let this blessed assurance control,
that Christ has regarded my helpless estate,
and has shed His own blood for my soul.

3 My sin – O the bliss of this glorious thought –
my sin – not in part – but the whole
is nailed to His cross; and I bear it no more;
praise the Lord, praise the Lord, O my soul.

4 For me, be it Christ, be it Christ hence to live!
if Jordan above me shall roll.
No pang shall be mine, for in death as in life
You will whisper Your peace to my soul.

5 But Lord, it's for You– for Your coming we wait,
the sky, not the grave, is our goal:
O trump of the angel! O voice of the Lord!
Blessed hope! blessed rest of my soul.

758   When the Lord in glory comes

GLORIOUS COMING   77 77 77 D

Words: Timothy Dudley-Smith
Music: Michael Baughen
and D G Wilson

1 When the Lord in glo-ry comes, not the trum-pets, not the
2 When the Lord is seen a-gain, not the glo-ries of His
3 When the Lord to hu-man eyes shall be-stride our nar-row

drums, not the an-them, not the psalm, not the
reign, not the light-nings through the storm, not the
skies, not the child of hum-ble birth, not the

thun-der, not the calm, not the shout the hea-vens
ra-diance of His form, not His pomp and power a-
car-pen-ter of earth, not the man by all de-

raise, not the cho-rus, not the praise,
-lone, not the splen-dours of His throne,
-nied, not the vic-tim cru-ci-fied,

759   When the trumpet of the Lord

ROLL CALL

Words and music: James M Black (1856–1938)

1 When the trum - pet of the Lord shall sound, and
2 On that bright and cloud - less morn - ing when the
3 Let us la - bour for the Mas - ter from the

time shall be no more, and the morn-ing breaks, e - ter - nal, bright, and
dead in Christ shall rise, and the glo - ry of His re - sur - rec - tion
dawn till set - ting sun, let us talk of all His won-derous love and

fair; when the saved of earth shall gath - er o - ver
share; when His cho - sen ones shall gath - er to their
care; then when all of life is o - ver, and our

on the oth - er shore, and the roll is called up yon-der, I'll be there.
home be-yond the skies, and the roll is called up yon-der, I'll be there.
work on earth is done, and the roll is called up yon-der, I'll be there.

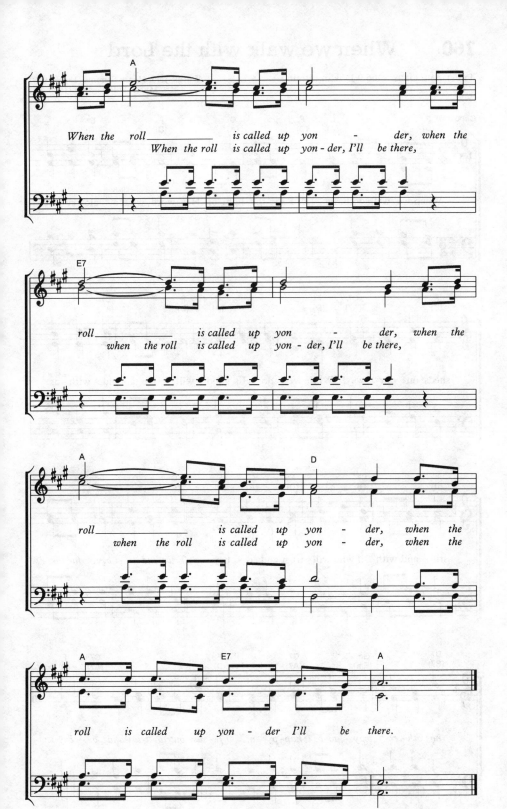

When the roll_____ is called up yon - der, when the
When the roll is called up yon - der, I'll be there,

roll_____ is called up yon - der, when the
when the roll is called up yon - der, I'll be there,

roll_____ is called up yon - der, when the
when the roll is called up yon - der, when the

roll is called up yon - der I'll be there.

760   When we walk with the Lord

TRUST AND OBEY   66 9 D with refrain

Words: John Henry Sammis (1846–1919)
Music: D B Towner (1833–96)

When we walk with the Lord in the light of His word, what a glo-ry He
sheds on our way! While we do His good will, He a-bides with us
still, and with all who will trust and o-bey. *Trust and o-bey, for there's*
no oth-er way to be hap-py in Je-sus, but to trust and o-bey.

1 When we walk with the Lord
in the light of His word,
what a glory He sheds on our way!
While we do His good will,
He abides with us still,
and with all who will trust and obey.
Trust and obey,
for there's no other way
to be happy in Jesus,
but to trust and obey.

2 Not a shadow can rise,
not a cloud in the skies,
but His smile quickly drives it away;
not a doubt nor a fear,
not a sigh nor a tear,
can abide while we trust and obey.
Trust and obey . . .

3 Not a burden we bear,
not a sorry we share,
but our toil He doth richly repay;
not a grief nor a loss,
not a frown nor a cross,
but is blest if we trust and obey.
Trust and obey . . .

4 But we never can prove
the delights of His love,
until all on the altar we lay;
for the favour He shows,
and the joy He bestows
are for them who will trust and obey.
Trust and obey . . .

5 Then in fellowship sweet,
we will sit at His feet,
or we'll walk by His side in the way.
What He says we will do,
where He sends we will go,
never fear, only trust and obey.
Trust and obey . . .

761 When to our world the Saviour came

Words: Timothy Dudley-Smith
Music: James W Elliott (1833–1915)

1 When to our world the Saviour came,
the sick and helpless heard His name;
and in their weakness longed to see
the healing Christ of Galilee.

2 That good physician! night and day
the people thronged about His way;
and wonder ran from soul to soul –
'The touch of Christ has made us whole!'

3 His praises then were heard and sung
by opened ears and loosened tongue,
while lightened eyes could see and know
the healing Christ of long ago.

4 Of long ago – yet living still,
who died for us on Calvary's hill;
who triumphed over cross and grave,
His healing hands stretched forth to save.

5 Those wounded hands are still the same,
and all who serve that saving Name
may share today in Jesus' plan –
the healing Christ of every man.

6 Then grant us, Lord, in this our day,
to hear the prayers the helpless pray;
give to us hearts their pain to share,
make of us hands to tend and care.

7 Make us Your hands! for Christ to live,
in prayer and service, swift to give;
till all the world rejoice to find
the healing Christ of all mankind.

Wherever I am

Words and music: Anon
Music arranged David Peacock

Quite fast

Wher-ev-er I am I'll praise Him, when-ev-er I

can I'll praise Him; for His love sur-

-rounds me like a sea; I'll praise the name of

Je - sus, lift up the name of Je - sus, for the

name of Je - sus lift - ed me.

763
Where the Lord walks

NAHUM

Based on the book of Nahum
Words and music: Anne Horrobin
and Sue Cartwright
Music arranged Phil Burt

Where the Lord walks, storms a-rise,_ the clouds are the dust raised by His feet;_ the earth shakes when the Lord ap-pears, the world and its peo-ple trem-ble.

You, Ni-ne-veh, are a wick-ed ci-ty, your

peo - ple _ plot a-gainst Me; you've made My peo - ple

D.C. al Fine

Is - ra - el suf - fer, but now I'm going to set them free.

Where the Lord walks, storms arise,
the clouds are the dust raised by His feet;
the earth shakes when the Lord appears,
the world and its people tremble.

1   You, Nineveh, are a wicked city,
     your people plot against Me;
     you've made My people Israel suffer,
     but now I'm going to set them free.
       Where the Lord walks . . .

2   The Lord will always protect His people,
     He'll care for those who trust Him;
     but turn against Him, oppose the Lord,
     and His judgement then is death.
       Where the Lord walks . . .

3   I say to my people Israel,
     a messenger is bringing good news;
     stand in the victory I've given you,
     for your enemy has been destroyed.
       Where the Lord walks . . .

764 While shepherds watched

WINCHESTER OLD   CM

Words: Nahum Tate (1652–1715)
Music: Tate's *Psalms*, 1592

While shep-herds watched their flocks by night, all seat-ed on the ground, the an-gel of the Lord came down and glo-ry shone a-round.

1 While shepherds watched their flocks by night,
    all seated on the ground,
    the angel of the Lord came down
    and glory shone around.

2 'Fear not,' said he – for mighty dread
    had seized their troubled mind –
    'Glad tidings of great joy I bring
    to you and all mankind:

3 'To you in David's town this day
    is born of David's line,
    a Saviour, who is Christ the Lord.
    And this shall be the sign:

4 'The heavenly babe you there shall find
    to human view displayed,
    all meanly wrapped in swaddling bands,
    and in a manger laid.'

5 Thus spake the angel; and forthwith
    appeared a shining throng
    of angels praising God, who thus
    addressed their joyful song:

6 'All glory be to God on high,
    and to the earth be peace;
    goodwill henceforth from heaven to men
    begin and never cease!'

765 Who can cheer the heart

ALL THAT THRILLS MY SOUL

Words and music: Thoro Harris

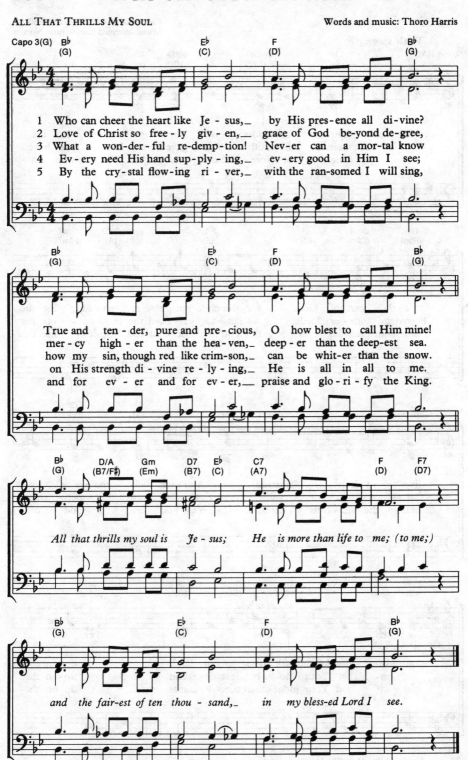

1 Who can cheer the heart like Je - sus,__ by His pres-ence all di-vine?
2 Love of Christ so free - ly giv - en,__ grace of God be-yond de-gree,
3 What a won-der-ful re-demp-tion! Nev-er can a mor-tal know
4 Ev - ery need His hand sup-ply - ing,__ ev-ery good in Him I see;
5 By the cry-stal flow-ing ri - ver,__ with the ran-somed I will sing,

True and ten - der, pure and pre - cious, O how blest to call Him mine!
mer - cy high - er than the hea - ven,__ deep - er than the deep-est sea.
how my sin, though red like crim-son,__ can be whit-er than the snow.
on His strength di - vine re - ly - ing,__ He is all in all to me.
and for ev - er and for ev - er,__ praise and glo - ri - fy the King.

All that thrills my soul is Je - sus; He is more than life to me; (to me;)

and the fair-est of ten thou - sand,__ in my bless-ed Lord I see.

Who can sound

Words and music: Graham Kendrick
Music arranged Christopher Norton

1 Who can sound the depths of sor - row in the
(2) scorned the truth You gave us, we have
(3) stand be - fore Your an - ger; who can

Fa - ther heart of God, for the child-ren we've re - ject - ed, for the
bowed to oth - er lords, we have sac - ri - ficed the child-ren on the
face Your pierc-ing eyes? For You love the weak and help-less, and You

lives so deep - ly scarred? And each light that we've ex -
al - tars of our gods. O let truth a - gain shine
hear the vic - tims' cries. Yes, You are a God of

- tin-guished has bought dark - ness to our land: up-on the
on us, let Your ho - ly fear de - scend: up-on the
just - ice, and Your judge-ment sure - ly comes: up-on the

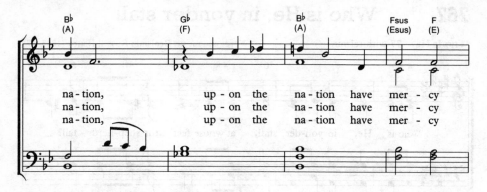

na - tion,   up - on the   na - tion have   mer - cy
na - tion,   up - on the   na - tion have   mer - cy
na - tion,   up - on the   na - tion have   mer - cy

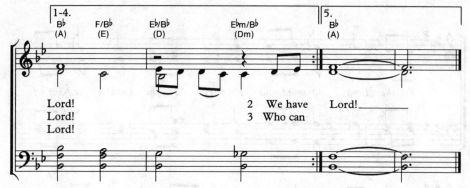

Lord!   2   We have   Lord!_____
Lord!   3   Who can
Lord!

1   Who can sound the depths of sorrow
in the Father heart of God,
for the children we've rejected,
for the lives so deeply scarred?
And each light that we've extinguished
has bought darkness to our land:
upon the nation, upon the nation
have mercy Lord!

2   We have scorned the truth You gave us,
we have bowed to other lords,
we have sacrificed the children
on the altars of our gods.
O let truth again shine on us,
let Your holy fear descend:
upon the nation, upon the nation
have mercy Lord!

MEN

3   Who can stand before Your anger;
who can face Your piercing eyes?
For You love the weak and helpless,
and You hear the victims' cries.

ALL

Yes, You are a God of justice,
and Your judgement surely comes:
upon the nation, upon the nation
have mercy Lord!

WOMEN

4   Who will stand against the violence?
Who will comfort those who mourn?
In an age of cruel rejection,
who will build for love a home?

ALL

Come and shake us into action,
come and melt our hearts of stone:
upon Your people, upon Your people,
have mercy Lord!

5   Who can sound the depths of mercy
in the Father heart of God?
For there is a Man of sorrows
who for sinners shed His blood.
He can heal the wounds of nations,
He can wash the guilty clean:
because of Jesus, because of Jesus,
have mercy Lord!

Who is He, in yonder stall

WHO IS HE   77 with refrain   Words and music: Benjamin Russell Hanby (1833–67)

1   Who is He, in yonder stall,
    at whose feet the shepherds fall?
      'Tis the Lord! O wondrous story!
      'Tis the Lord! the King of Glory!
      At His feet we humbly fall;
      crown Him, crown Him Lord of all.

2   Who is He, in yonder cot,
    bending to His toilsome lot?
      'Tis the Lord . . .

3   Who is He, in deep distress,
    fasting in the wilderness?
      'Tis the Lord . . .

4   Who is He, that stands and weeps
    at the grave where Lazarus sleeps?
      'Tis the Lord . . .

5   Lo, at midnight, who is He
    prays in dark Gethsemane?
      'Tis the Lord . . .

6   Who is He, in Calvary's throes,
    asks for blessings on His foes?
      'Tis the Lord . . .

7   Who is He that from the grave
    comes to heal and help and save?
      'Tis the Lord . . .

8   Who is He that from His throne
    rules through all the worlds alone?
      'Tis the Lord . . .

768 # Who is like unto Thee

Words and music: popular version of original by
Judy Horner Montemayor
Music arranged Roland Fudge

Alternative guitar chords for use
without piano part, in brackets

Who is like un-to Thee,_____ O____ Lord a-mong gods?_____

Who is like un-to Thee?_____ Glo-rious in

ho-li-ness, fear-ful in prais-es, do-ing

won-ders;_____ who_ is like un-to Thee?_____

769   Who is on the Lord's side?

ARMAGEDDON   65 65 D with refrain

Words: Frances Ridley Havergal (1836–79)
Music: J Goss (1800–80)

Who is on the Lord's side? Who will serve the King? Who will be His help-ers oth-er lives to bring? Who will leave the world's side? Who will face the foe? Who is on the Lord's side? Who for Him will go? By Thy call of mer-cy, by Thy grace di-vine, we are on the Lord's side;_ Sav-iour, we are Thine.

1 Who is on the Lord's side?
Who will serve the King?
Who will be His helpers
other lives to bring?
Who will leave the world's side?
Who will face the foe?
Who is on the Lord's side?
Who for Him will go?
By Thy call of mercy,
by Thy grace divine,
we are on the Lord's side;
Saviour, we are Thine.

2 Not for weight of glory,
not for crown or palm,
enter we the army,
raise the warrior-psalm;
but for love that claimeth
lives for whom He died:
he whom Jesus nameth
must be on His side.
By Thy love constraining,
by Thy grace divine,
we are on the Lord's side;
Saviour, we are Thine.

3 Fierce may be the conflict,
strong may be the foe,
but the King's own army
none can overthrow.
Round His standard ranging,
victory is secure,
for His truth unchanging
makes the triumph sure.
Joyfully enlisting,
by Thy grace divine,
we are on the Lord's side;
Saviour, we are Thine.

4 Chosen to be soldiers
in an alien land,
chosen, called, and faithful,
for our captain's band;
in the service royal
let us not grow cold;
let us be right loyal,
noble, true and bold.
Master, Thou wilt keep us,
by Thy grace divine,
always on the Lord's side,
Saviour, always Thine.

770

Will your anchor hold

Words: Priscilla Jane Owens (1829–99)
Music: W J Kirkpatrick (1838–1921)

Will your an-chor hold in the storms of life, when the clouds un-fold their

wings of strife? When the strong tides lift, and the ca - bles strain, will your

an-chor drift, or__ firm re-main? *We have an an-chor that keeps the soul*

stead-fast and sure while the bil - lows roll; fast-ened to the rock which

can - not move, ground-ed firm and deep in the Sav - iour's love!

1 Will your anchor hold in the storms of life,
   when the clouds unfold their wings of strife?
   When the strong tides lift, and the cables strain,
   will your anchor drift, or firm remain?
   We have an anchor that keeps the soul
   steadfast and sure while the billows roll;
   fastened to the rock which cannot move,
   grounded firm and deep in the Saviour's love!

2 Will your anchor hold in the straits of fear,
   when the breakers roar and the reef is near?
   While the surges rage, and the wild winds blow,
   shall the angry waves then your bark o'erflow?
   We have an anchor . . .

3 Will your anchor hold in the floods of death,
   when the waters cold chill your latest breath?
   On the rising tide you can never fail,
   while your anchor holds within the veil.
   We have an anchor . . .

4 Will your eyes behold through the morning light,
   the city of gold and the harbour bright?
   Will you anchor safe by the heavenly shore,
   when life's storms are past for evermore?
   We have an anchor . . .

771 Wind, wind blow on me

WIND WIND

Words and music: Jane and Betsy Clowe
Music arranged David Peacock

Wind, wind blow on me;__ wind, wind set me free!__

Wind, wind my Fa-ther sent the bless-èd Ho-ly Spi-rit.____

Je-sus told us all a-bout You, how we could not live with-out_ You;

with His blood the pow-er bought to help us live the life He taught.

Wind, wind blow on me;
wind, wind set me free!
Wind, wind my Father sent
the blessèd Holy Spirit.

1 Jesus told us all about You,
   how we could not live without You;
   with His blood the power bought
   to help us live the life He taught.
   Wind, wind . . .

2 When we're weary You console us,
   when we're lonely You enfold us,
   when in danger You uphold us,
   blessèd Holy Spirit.
   Wind, wind . . .

3 When into the church You came,
   it was not in Your own but Jesus' name:
   Jesus Christ is still the same –
   He sends the Holy Spirit.
   Wind, wind . . .

4 Set us free to love our brothers,
   set us free to live for others,
   that the world the Son might see,
   and Jesus' name exalted be.
   Wind, wind . . .

772

With all my heart

Words and music: Paul Field
Music arranged Christopher Norton

Lord.

2 With
3 With

⊕ CODA

Lord.

1 With all my heart I thank You Lord.
With all my heart I thank You Lord.
For this bread and wine we break,
for this sacrament we take,
for the forgiveness that You make,
I thank You Lord.

2 With all my soul I thank You Lord.
With all my soul I thank You Lord.
For this victory that You've won,
for this taste of things to come,
for this love that makes us one,
I thank You Lord.

3 With all my voice I thank You Lord.
With all my voice I thank You Lord.
For the sacrifice of pain,
for the Spirit and the flame,
for the power of Your name,
I thank You Lord.

773   With harps and viols

THE NEW SONG   11 12 with refrain

Words: Arthur Tappan Pierson (1837–1911)
Music: Philip Bliss (1838–76)

1 With harps and with viols
        there stand a great throng
in the presence of Jesus,
        and sing this new song:
    Unto Him who has loved us
    and washed us from sin,
    unto Him be the glory
    for ever! Amen.

2 All these once were sinners,
        defiled in His sight,
now arrayed in pure garments
        in praise they unite:
    Unto Him who has . . .

3 He's made of the rebel
        a priest and a king,
He has bought us, and taught us
        this new song to sing:
    Unto Him who has . . .

4 How helpless and hopeless
        we sinners had been,
if He never had loved us
        till cleansed from our sin!
    Unto Him who has . . .

5 Aloud in His praises
        our voices shall ring,
so that others, believing,
        this new song shall sing:
    Unto Him who has . . .

774   With joy we meditate the grace

St Stephen   CM

Words: Isaac Watts (1614–1748) altd.
Music: William Jones (1726–1800)

1 With joy we meditate the grace
  of our High Priest above;
His heart is made of tenderness,
  it overflows with love.

2 Touched with a sympathy within,
  He knows our feeble frame;
He knows what sore temptations mean,
  for He has felt the same.

3 He, in the days of feeble flesh,
  poured out His cries and tears;
and now exalted feels afresh
  what every member bears.

4 He'll never quench the smoking flax,
  but raise it to a flame;
the bruisèd reed He never breaks,
  nor scorns the meanest name.

5 Then let our humble faith address
  His mercy and His power;
we shall obtain delivering grace
  in the distressing hour.

775   With my heart I worship You

Words and music: Norman Warren

ALTERNATIVE VERSES:

With my lips I praise You . . .

With my life I serve You . . .

776 Wonderful Counsellor

Words and music: Paul Armstrong

Won-der-ful_ Coun-sel-lor,_ the Migh-ty God,_____ the
Ev - er - last-ing Fa-ther, the Prince_ of Peace, the Prince of
Peace, the Ev - er - last-ing Fa-ther, the Migh - ty
God._____ Won-der-ful_ Coun-sel-lor,_

777 Wonderful Counsellor, Jesus

Words and music: Bill Yarger

Tenderly

1 Won-der-ful
2 Migh-ty God,
3 Ev - er - last - ing
4 Prince of Peace,
5 Won-der-ful

Coun-sel-lor___ Je - sus:
Son of God, Je - sus;
Fa - ther, Je - sus;
rule my heart, Je - sus;
Coun-sel-lor___ Je - sus;

search me, know___ me, Je - sus;
Name a-bove all o - ther names, Je - sus:
Ho - ly and___ un - change-a-ble, Je - sus:
know my ev - ery an-xious thought, Je - sus;
Migh-ty God, Son of God, Je - sus;

Words and music: © Maranatha! Music (USA)/Word Music (UK), (a division of Word (UK) Ltd)
9 Holdom Avenue, Bletchley, Milton Keynes MK1 1QR, UK
For British Isles, Republic of Ireland, Continent of Europe (Exc Benelux)

1 Wonderful Counsellor Jesus:
   search me, know me, Jesus;
   lead me, guide me, Jesus –
   Wonderful Counsellor Jesus.

2 Mighty God, Son of God, Jesus;
   Name above all other names, Jesus:
   glorify, magnify, Jesus –
   Mighty God, Son of God, Jesus.

3 Everlasting Father, Jesus;
   Holy and unchangeable, Jesus:
   fill me with Your presence, Jesus –
   Everlasting Father, Jesus.

4 Prince of Peace, rule my heart, Jesus;
   know my every anxious thought, Jesus;
   calm my fears, dry my tears, Jesus –
   Prince of Peace, rule my heart, Jesus.

5 Wonderful Counsellor Jesus;
   Mighty God, Son of God, Jesus;
   Everlasting Father, Jesus –
   Prince of Peace, rule my heart, Jesus.

778 Within the veil

Words and music: Ruth Dryden

Within the veil I now would come, into the holy place to look upon Thy face. I see such beauty there, no other can compare, I worship Thee, my Lord, within the veil.

779 Worthy art thou, O Lord

Words and music: Dave Richards
Music arranged Roger Mayor

Wor-thy art Thou, O Lord, our God, of hon-our and power, for You are reign - ing now on high, Hal-le-lu - jah. Je-sus is Lord of all the earth, Hal-le - lu - jah, hal-le-lu - jah, hal-le-lu - jah.

780 Worthy is the Lamb

Music arranged Roland Fudge

1 Worthy is the Lamb;
  Worthy is the Lamb;
  Worthy is the Lamb;
  Worthy is the Lamb.

2 Holy is the Lamb . . .

3 Precious is the Lamb . . .

4 Praises to the Lamb . . .

5 Glory to the Lamb . . .

6 Jesus is our Lamb . . .

781 Worthy is the Lamb seated

Words and music: David J Hadden

Wor-thy is the Lamb seat-ed on the throne, wor-thy is the Lamb who was slain, to re- -ceive po-wer and rich-es, and wis-dom and strength, hon-our and glo-ry, glo-ry and praise, for ev-er and ev-er-more.

782   Worthy, O worthy are You Lord

Words and music: Mark S Kinzer

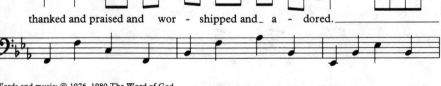

Flowing

Capo 3(C)

Wor-thy, O wor-thy are You Lord, wor-thy to be thanked and praised and wor - shipped and a - dored; wor-thy, O wor - thy are You Lord, wor-thy to be thanked and praised and wor - shipped and a - dored.

783 Ye holy angels bright

DARWELL'S 148TH   66 66 44 44

Words: Richard Baxter (1615–91) and others
Music: John Darwell (1731–89)

Ye ho - ly an - gels bright, who wait at God's right hand, or through the realms of___ light fly___ at your Lord's com - mand, as - sist our song, or else the theme too high doth seem for mor - tal tongue.

1   Ye holy angels bright,
    who wait at God's right hand,
    or through the realms of light
    fly at your Lord's command,
        assist our song,
        or else the theme
        too high doth seem
        for mortal tongue.

2   Ye blessèd souls at rest,
    who see your Saviour's face,
    whose glory, e'en the least
    is far above our grace,
        God's praises sound,
        as in His sight
        with sweet delight
        ye do abound.

3   Ye saints, who toil below,
    adore your heavenly King,
    and onward as ye go
    some joyful anthem sing;
        take what He gives
        and praise Him still,
        through good and ill,
        who ever lives!

4   My soul, bear thou thy part,
    triumph in God above:
    and with a well-tuned heart
    sing thou the songs of love!
        Let all thy days
        till life shall end,
        whate'er He send,
        be filled with praise.

784   Ye servants of God

LAUDATE DOMINUM   55 55 65 65

Words: Charles Wesley (1707–88)
Music: C H H Parry (1848–1918)

1 Ye servants of God,
your Master proclaim,
and publish abroad
His wonderful name;
the name all-victorious
of Jesus extol;
His kingdom is glorious,
and rules over all.

2 God ruleth on high,
almighty to save;
and still He is nigh,
His presence we have;
the great congregation
His triumph shall sing,
ascribing salvation
to Jesus our King.

3 'Salvation to God
who sits on the throne',
let all cry aloud,
and honour the Son:
the praises of Jesus
the angels proclaim,
fall down on their faces,
and worship the Lamb.

4 Then let us adore,
and give Him His right –
all glory and power,
all wisdom and might:
all honour and blessing,
with angels above;
and thanks never-ceasing,
and infinite love.

785 Yes, power belongs to You, O Lord

Words and music: Colin Preston
Music arranged Chris Mitchell

Yes, power be-longs to You, O Lord, in You we put our trust; You are sove-reign o - ver all,_ great are You. Great in Your mer - cy, Lord, great in Your love, a migh-ty war-rior in whom we trust.

786

Yes, God is good

Williams LM

Words: John Hampden Gurney (1802–62)
Music: from *Templi Carmina*, 1829

1 Yes, God is good – in earth and sky,
from ocean depths and spreading wood,
ten thousand voices seem to cry:
God made us all, and God is good.

2 The sun that keeps his trackless way,
and downward pours his golden flood,
night's sparkling hosts, all seem to say
in accents clear that God is good.

3 The joyful birds prolong the strain,
their song with every spring renewed;
the air we breathe, and falling rain,
each softly whispers: God is good.

4 I hear it in the rushing breeze;
the hills that have for ages stood,
the echoing sky and roaring seas,
all swell the chorus: God is good.

5 Yes, God is good, all nature says,
by God's own hand with speech endued;
and man, in louder notes of praise,
should sing for joy that God is good.

6 For all Your gifts we bless You, Lord,
but chiefly for our heavenly food,
Your pardoning grace, Your quickening word,
these prompt our song, that God is good.

Yesterday, today, for ever

788 You are beautiful

Words and music: Mark Altrogge
Music arranged Christopher Norton

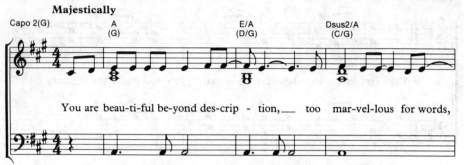

You are beau-ti-ful be-yond des-crip - tion,___ too mar-vel-lous for words,

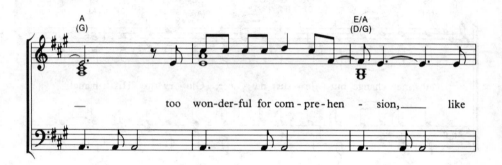

___ too won-der-ful for com - pre-hen - sion,___ like

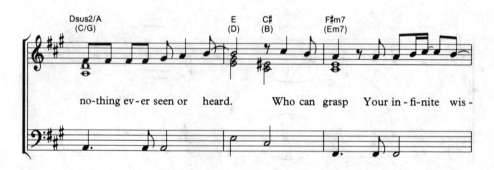

no-thing ev-er seen or heard. Who can grasp Your in-fi-nite wis-

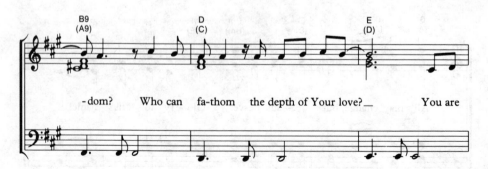

-dom? Who can fa-thom the depth of Your love?___ You are

beau-ti-ful be-yond des-crip - tion, Ma-jes-ty,___ en-throned a - bove.

And I stand, I stand in awe of You;___ I

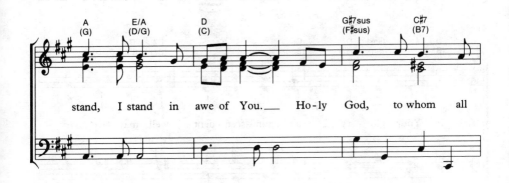

stand, I stand in awe of You.___ Ho-ly God, to whom all

praise is due, I stand in awe of You.

789 You are coming

BEVERLEY 87 887 77 77

Words: Frances Ridley Havergal (1836–79)
altered Horrobin/Leavers
Music: William Henry Monk (1823–89)

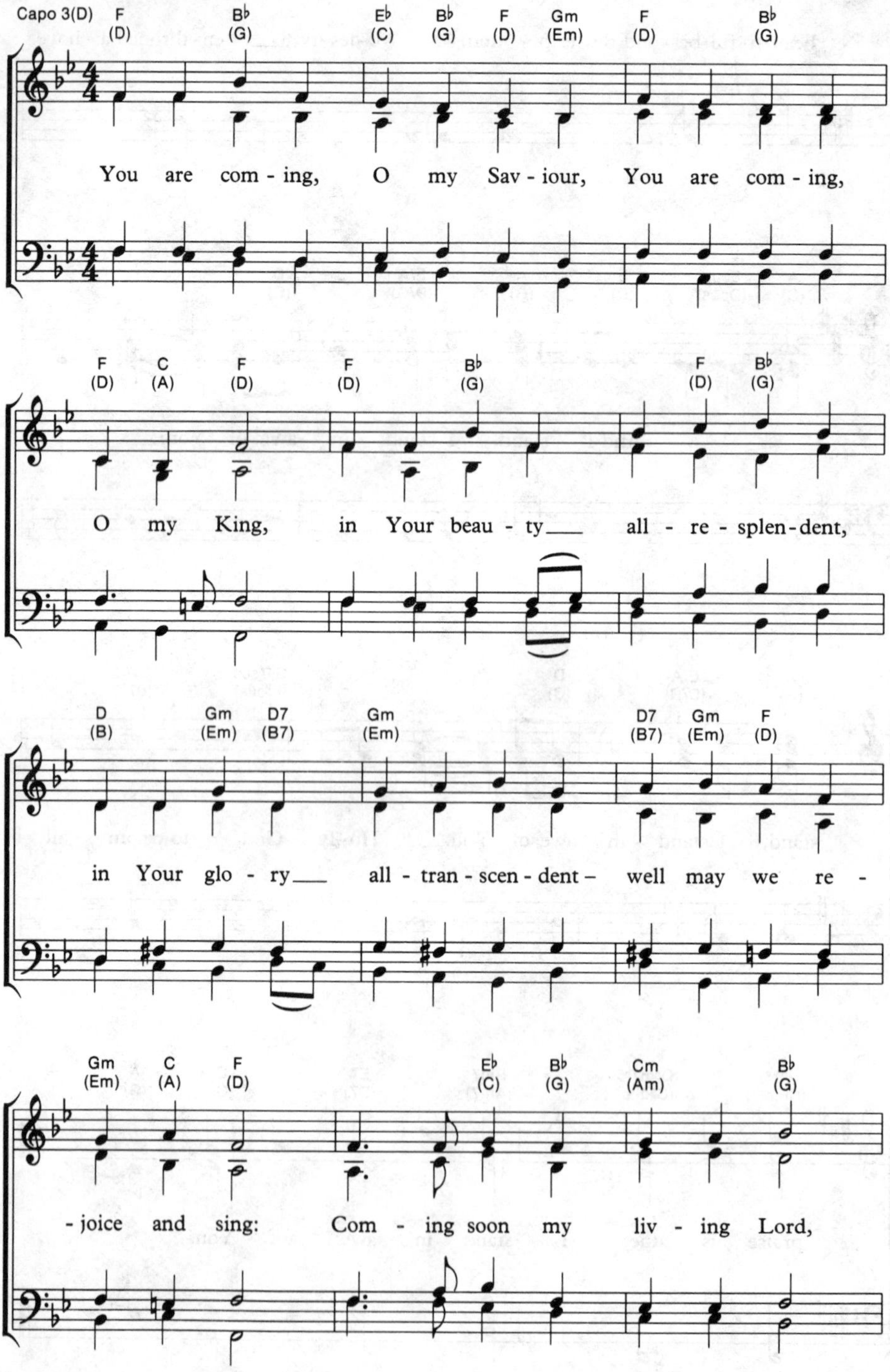

Capo 3(D)
F (D) B♭ (G) E♭ (C) B♭ (G) F (D) Gm (Em) F (D) B♭ (G)
You are com - ing, O my Sav - iour, You are com - ing,
F (D) C (A) F (D) F (D) B♭ (G) F (D) B♭ (G)
O my King, in Your beau - ty all - re - splen - dent,
D (B) Gm (Em) D7 (B7) Gm (Em) D7 (B7) Gm (Em) F (D)
in Your glo - ry all - tran - scen - dent – well may we re -
Gm (Em) C (A) F (D) E♭ (C) B♭ (G) Cm (Am) B♭ (G)
- joice and sing: Com - ing soon my liv - ing Lord,

her - alds sing Your glo - rious praise; com - ing! now on___ earth a - dored, songs of tri - umph we shall raise.

1   You are coming, O my Saviour,
    You are coming, O my King,
    in Your beauty all-resplendent,
    in Your glory all-transcendent –
    well may we rejoice and sing:
    Coming soon my living Lord,
    heralds sing Your glorious praise;
    coming! now on earth adored,
    songs of triumph we shall raise.

2   You are coming, You are coming,
    we shall meet You on Your way,
    we shall see You, we shall see You,
    we shall bless You, we shall show You
    all our hearts could never say.
    What an anthem that will be,
    ringing out eternally,
    earth's and heaven's praises meet,
    at Your own all glorious feet!

3   O the joy to see You reigning,
    You, my own belovèd Lord!
    Every tongue Your name confessing,
    worship, honour, glory blessing
    brought to You with glad accord –
    You, my Master and my Friend,
    vindicated and enthroned,
    unto earth's remotest end
    glorified, adored, and owned!

790   You are the King of glory

Words and music: Mavis Ford

You are the King of glo - ry, You are the Prince of
Peace, You are the Lord of heaven and earth,
You're the Son of right-eous - ness. An - gels bow down be -
- fore___ You, wor - ship and a - dore, for
You have the words of e - ter - nal life,___ You are Je - sus Christ the

Lord. Ho-san-na to the Son of Da-vid! Ho-san-na to the King of kings! Glo-ry in the high-est hea-ven, for Je-sus the Mes-si-ah reigns!

You are the King of glory,
You are the Prince of Peace,
You are the Lord of heaven and earth,
You're the Son of righteousness.
Angels bow down before You,
worship and adore,
for You have the words of eternal life,
You are Jesus Christ the Lord.
Hosanna to the Son of David!
Hosanna to the King of kings!
Glory in the highest heaven,
for Jesus the Messiah reigns!

791

You are the mighty King

Words and music: Eddie Espinosa
Music arranged Roger Mayor

You are the migh - ty King,

the liv - ing ___ Word;

mas - ter of ev - ery - thing –

You ___ are the Lord.

Fine

And I praise Your name,

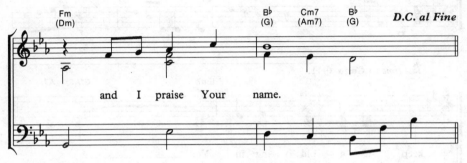

D.C. al Fine

and I praise Your name.

1 You are the mighty King,
the living Word;
master of everything –
You are the Lord.
And I praise Your name,
and I praise Your name.

2 You are almighty God,
Saviour and Lord;
Wonderful Counsellor,
You are the Lord.
And I praise Your name,
and I praise Your name.

3 You are the Prince of Peace,
Emmanuel;
Everlasting Father,
You are the Lord.
And I love Your name,
and I love Your name.

4 You are the mighty King,
the living Word;
master of everything,
You are the Lord.

792   You are the Vine

Words and music: Danny Daniels
Music arranged Christopher Norton

Words and music: © 1982 Mercy Publishing,
administered in Europe by Thankyou Music,
PO Box 75, Eastbourne, East Sussex BN23 6NW, UK

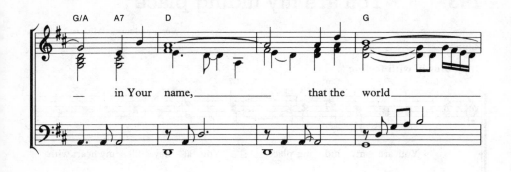

in Your name,_____ that the world_____

___ will sure - ly know_____ that You have

pow - er   to   heal   and   to   save._____

D.C. al Coda

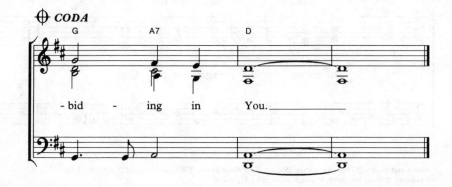

CODA

- bid - ing   in   You._____

793   You are my hiding place

Words and music: Michael Ledner

Round

Slowly with feeling

You are my hid - ing place,____ You al - ways fill my heart with

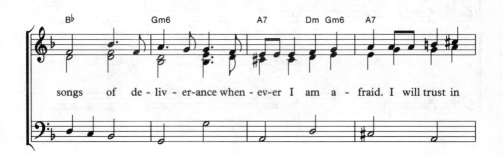

songs of de - liv - er-ance when - ev-er I am a - fraid. I will trust in

You,_____ I will trust in You,_____ let the weak say:

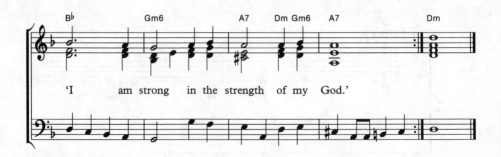

'I   am strong in the strength of my God.'

794

You are worthy

Words and music: John Daniel Lawtum

795 You laid aside Your majesty

Words and music: Noel Richards
Music arranged Roger Mayor

You laid a - side Your ma - jes - ty, gave up ev - ery-thing for me, suf-fered at the hands of those You had cre - a - ted; You took all my guilt and shame, when You died__ and rose a - gain;__ now to-day__ You reign in

heaven and earth ex - alt - ed. I real-ly want to wor-ship You, my

Lord, You have won my heart and I am Yours for ev-er and ev - er:

I will love You. You are the on-ly one who died for

me, gave Your life___ to set me free, so I lift my voice to You

___ in a-do-ra - tion.___

796   You shall go out with joy

Words and music: Stuart Dauermann
Music arranged Roland Fudge

With joy

You shall go out with joy— and be led forth with peace, and the

moun-tains and the hills shall break forth be - fore you. There'll be

shouts of joy— and the trees of the field shall— clap, shall clap their

hands, and the trees of the field shall clap their hands, and the

trees of the field shall clap their hands, and the trees of the field shall

clap their hands, and you'll go out with joy.

You shall go out with joy
    and be led forth with peace,
and the mountains and the hills
    shall break forth before you.
There'll be shouts of joy
    and the trees of the field
shall clap, shall clap their hands,
and the trees of the field
    shall clap their hands,
and the trees of the field
    shall clap their hands,
and the trees of the field
    shall clap their hands,
and you'll go out with joy.

797 Your love is to me

Words and music: Richard Taylor
Music arranged Phil Burt

Your_ love is to me like an ev-er-flow-ing stream, Your love is to me like an ev-er-flow-ing stream, reach-ing out Lord.___ Lord we need Your love, yes, we need Your

love, we need Your love to make it through;____

____ Lord we need Your love, yes, we need Your

love, we need Your love to make it through.____

Your love is to me like an ever-flowing stream,
Your love is to me like an ever-flowing stream,
Your love is to me like an ever-flowing stream
reaching out Lord.

Lord we need Your love,
yes, we need Your love,
we need Your love to make it through;
Lord we need Your love,
yes, we need Your love,
we need Your love to make it through.

798 Yours, Lord, is the greatness

Words and music: Helen Thomas
Music arranged Andy Silver
and Christopher Norton

2 All riches and honour come from You;
  You are our God, You make us strong.
      Yours, Lord . . .

3 And now, our God, we give You thanks,
  we praise Your glorious name.
      Yours, Lord . . .

"Let us praise God's glory"

Ephesians 1:12

Copyright Addresses

Alexanders Copyright Trust, c/o S W Grant, 12 Lawrie Park Crescent, Sydenham, London SE26 6HD

American Catholic Press, 16160 South Seton Drive, South Holland, IL 60473 USA

M C & M M Austin, 4 Burkes Close, Beaconsfield, Bucks. HP9 1ES

J M Barnes, 15 South Canterbury Road, Canterbury, Kent CT1 3LH

Cliff Barrows, Melody Lane, Rt 9 No Parker Road, Greenville, SC 2960 USA

Bible Society, Stonehill Green, Westlea Down, Swindon SN5 7DG

A & C Black (Publishers) Ltd, Howard Road, Eaton Socon, Huntington, Cambs. PE19 3EZ

Fred Bock Music, PO Box 333 Tarzana, CA 91356 USA

Boosey & Hawkes Music Publishers, 295 Regent Street, London W1R 8JH

Gordon Brattle, c/o N A M Cooke, 52 Birch Grove, Ealing Common, London W3 9SR

Breitkopf & Hartel, Buch-und Musikverlag, Walkmühl Strasse 52, D-6200 Weisbaden 1, W Germany

R Browne, 5 Avondale Road, Trowbridge, Wiltshire

E J Burns, Christ Church Vicarage, 6 Watling Street Road, Fulwood, Preston, Lancs. PR2 4DY

Catacombs Productions, J S Craggs Management Services, PO Box 4124 Station A, Victoria, BC V8X 3X4 Canada

Canticle Publications, c/o House Group Music, 2712 West 104th Terrace, Leaworth, IL 66236 USA

Central Board of Finance of the Church of England, Church House, Great Smith Street, London SW1

K Chance, Glaubensentrum, Gruner Plaz 12, 3340 Wolfenbuttel, W Germany

Chappell Music, 129 Park Street, London W1Y 3EA

Cherry Lane Music Ltd, 75 High Street, Needham Market, Ipswich, Suffolk 1P6 8AN

Christian Fellowship of Columbia, 4600 Christian Fellowship Road, Columbia, MS 65203 USA

Paul S Deeming, 8987 St Louis Avenue, St Louis, MS 63114 USA

Colin C Duckworth, 44 Margerson Road, Ben Rhydding, Ilkley, West Yorks. LS29 8QD

Timothy Dudley-Smith, Rectory Meadow, Bramerton, Norwich NR14 7DW

E M Dyke, 32 Woodlands Close, Harrogate, N. Yorks. HG2 7AZ

William Elkin Music Services, Station Road Industrial Estate, Salhouse, Norwich, Norfolk NR13 6NY

Paul Field, 26 Demesne Road, Wallington, Surrey SM6 8PP

Franciscan Communications, 1229 South Santee Street, Los Angeles, CA 90015 USA

Gaither Music Company, Copyright Management, PO Box 737, Alexandria, IN 46001, USA

GIA Publications Inc, 7404 S. Mason Avenue, Chicago, IL 60638 USA

J S Graggs Management Services, PO Box 4124, Station A, Victoria BC V8X 3X4, Canada

Gospel Publishing House, 1445 Boonville Avenue, Springfield, MS 65802 USA

D R Gould, 34 Pollards Drive, Horsham, West Sussex RH16 4AL

Jeanne Harper, Stanfords, 27 Munster Green, Haywards Heath, West Sussex RH16 4AL

David Higham Associates, 5–8 Lower John Street, Golden Square, London W1R 4HA

High-Fye Music, Campbell Connelly Co Ltd, 8–9 Frith Street, London W1V 5TZ

Hope Publishing, 380 South Main Place, Carol Stream, IL 60188 USA

Hymns Ancient & Modern, St Mary's Works, St Mary's Plain, Norwich, Norfolk NR3 3BH

Integrity's Hosanna! Music, Glyndley Manor, Stone Cross, Pevensey, East Sussex BN24 5BS

International Music Publications, Woodford Trading Estate, Southend Road, Woodford Green, Essex IG8 8HN

InterVarsity Press, 5206 Main Street, PO Box 1400, Downers End, IL 60515 USA

John Ireland Trust, 35 St Mary's Mansions, St Mary's Terrace. London W2 1SQ

W F Jabusch, University of St Mary of the Lake, Mundelein Seminary, Mundelein, IL 60060 USA

Francis Jackson, Nether Garth, Acklam, Moulton, Yorks. YR7 9RG

A M Jones, 22 Wentworth Road, Chilwell, Nottingham NG9 4FP

Roger Jones (Christian Music Ministries), 325 Bromford Road, Hodge Hill, Birmingham B36 8ET

Jubilate Hymns, c/o 61 Chessel Avenue, Southampton S02 4DY

Kenwood Music, Lifestyle Music Ltd, PO Box 356, Leighton Buzzard, Beds. LU7 8WP

B K M Kerr, Wayside Cottage, Friston Hill, East Dene, Eastbourne, East Sussex BN20 0BP

Bob Kilpatrick Music, PO Box 493194, Redding, CA 96049 USA

Lindsey Music, 23 Hitchin Street, Biggleswade, Beds. SG18 8AX

Manna Music Inc, 25510 Avenue Stanford, Suite 101, Valencia, CA 91355 USA

Andrew Maries, St Cuthbert's Centre, Peasholme Green, York YO1 2PW

Dr John Marsh, The Vicarage, 36 Manor Road, Ossett, West Yorkshire WF5 0AU

Marshall Morgan & Scott, Middlesex House, 34–42 Cleveland Street, London W1P 5FB

Kevin Mayhew Ltd, The Paddock, Rattlesbury, Bury St Edmunds, Suffolk

Meadowgreen MusicIMP, Woodford Trading Estate, Southend Road, Woodford Green, Essex IG8 8HN

Methodist Church Division of Education & Youth, 2 Chester House, Pages Lane, Muswell Hill, London N10 1PR

Methodist Publishing House, 20 Ivatt Way, Peterborough, Cambs. PE3 7PG

Rev Roland Meredith, The Rectory, 13 Station Road, Witney, Oxfordshire OX8 6BH

Moody Bible Insititute, 820 N. La Salle Street, Chicago, IL 60610 USA

A R Mowbray Ltd, Artillery House, Artillery Row, London SW1P 1RT

Music Publishing International, 75 High Street, Needham Market, Suffolk IP6 8AN

Mustard Seed Music, Lifestyle Music Ltd, PO Box 356, Leighton Buzzard, Beds. LU7 8WP

National Young Life Campaign, Spring Cottage, Spring Road, Leeds, West Yorks. LF6 1AD

Nazarene Publishing House, Box 419527, Kansas City, MO 64141 USA

New Song Ministries, PO Box 11662, Costa Mesa, CA 92627 USA

Novello & Co Ltd, 8–10 Lower James Street, London W1R 3PL

Overseas Missionary Fellowship, 2 Cluny Road, Singapore 1025, Republic of Singapore

Oxford University Press, Music Department, Walton Street, Oxford OX2 6DP

Patch Music/Peer Music, Peer-Southern Organisation, 8 Denmark Street, London WC1 8LT

Colin Preston, 81 Howth Drive, Woodley, Reading, Berks.

The Public Trustee Office, Stewart House, Kingsway, London WC2B 6JX

M E Rees, 5a Thornwood Road, Epping, Essex CM16 6SX

Restoration Music Ltd, Lifestyle Music Ltd, PO Box 356, Leighton Buzzard, Beds. LU7 8WP

John Richards, Renewal Servicing, PO Box 17, Shepperton, Middlesex TW17 8NU

Joan Robinson, 47 Woodlands Road, Beaumont, Lancaster

Rocksmith Music/Leosong Copyright Service, 7–8 Greenland Place, London NW1 0AT

R Rusbridge, 9 Springfield House, Cotham Road, Bristol BS6 6DQ

Salvationist Publishing & Supplies Ltd, 117–121 Judd Street, London WC1H 9NN

Pete Sanchez Jnr, 4723 Hickory Downs, Houston, TX 77084 USA

Scripture Gift Mission, Radstock House, 3 Ecclestone Street, London SW1W 9LZ

Scripture Union, 130 City Road, London EC1V 2NJ

Signalgrade Music Ltd, 48 Chatsworth Avenue, Raynes Park, London SW20 8JZ

C Simmonds, School House, 81 Clapham Road, Bedford MK41 7RB

Stainer & Bell Ltd, PO Box 110, 82 High Road, London N2 9PW

Straightway Music, Gaither Copyright Management, PO Box 737, Alexandria, IN 46001 USA

C L Taylor, 59 Baldwin Avenue, Eastbourne, East Sussex

Thankyou Music Ltd, 1 St Annes Road, Eastbourne, East Sussex BN21 3UN

Gordon Thompson Music, a division of Warner/Chappell Music Canada Ltd, 85 Scarsdale Road, Unit 101, Don Mills, Ontario, M3B 2R2 Canada

J Tyrrell, 41 Minster Road, Godalming, Surrey

Josef Weinberger Ltd, 12–14 Mortimer Street, London W1N 7RD

Whole Armor Publishing, 2828 Azalea Place, Nashville, TN 37204 USA

Word Music (UK) Ltd, 9 Holdom Avenue, Bletchley, Milton Keynes MK1 1QU

Word of God Music, PO Box 8617, Ann Arbor, MI 48107 USA

Youth with a Mission, Schloss Hurlach, 8931 Hurlach I, W. Germany

Phil Burt, Roland Fudge, Ruth Hooke, Peter Horrobin, Horrobin/Leavers, Anne Horrobin, Greg Leavers, Andy Silver, c/o Marshall Pickering, Middlesex House, 34–42 Cleveland Street, London W1P 5FB

USA and Canada

Benson Company Inc, 365 Great Circle Road, Nashville, TN 37228 USA

C A Music Services, 2021 N Brower, Simi Valley, CA 93065 USA

Celebration Music, Maranatha! Music, PO Box 1396, Costa Mesa, CA 92628 USA

Fairhill Music, PO Box 933, Newbury Park, CA 91320 USA

Friends First Music, Dawn Treader Music, Straightway Music, Gaither Copyright Management, PO Box 737, Alexandria, IN 46001 USA

Latter Rain Music, Sparrow Corporation, PO Box 2120, 9255 Deering Avenue, Chatsworth, CA 91311 USA

LexiconSpectra Music Copyright Management Inc., 1102 17th Avenue South, Suite 400, Nashville, TN 57212 USA

Lillenas Publishing Company, Box 419527, Kansas City, MO 64141 USA

Meadowgreen Music Inc, 8 Music Square West, Nashville, TN 37202 USA

Mercy Publishing, PO Box 65004, Ahaheim, CA 92815 USA

People of Destiny, 7881-8 Beechcroft Avenue, Gaithersbury, MO 20879 USA

Rocksmith Music, c/o Trust Music Management, 6255 Sunset Blvd, Suite 723, Hollywood, CA 90028 USA

RodeheaverNorman Claydon Publishing, Word Inc, 5221 N O'Connor Blvd, Suite 1000, Irving, TX 75039 USA

Star Song Music, 2325 Crestmoor, Nashville, TN 37215 USA

Timothy Dudley-Smith, Jubilate Hymns, Hope Publishing Company, 380 South Main Place, Carol Stream, IL 60188 USA

Warner Chappell Music Corp, 9000 Sunset Boulvard, Los Angeles, CA 90069, USA

Word Music, c/o Word Inc, 5221 N O'Connor Boulvard, Suite 1000, Irving, TX 75039 USA

Rest of world

Acts Music, c/o New Spilkins Pharmacy, 187 Main Street, Kenilworth, Johannesburg 2190, Republic of South Africa

Australia and New Zealand

Genesis Music, PO Box 26, Auburn 2144, Australia

Maranatha! Music, Thankyou Music, Integrity's Hosanna! Music, Mercy Publishing, Restoration Music, Canticle Publications, Celebration, Scripture in Song, Scripture in Song, PO Box 17161, Greenlane, Auckland, New Zealand

Straightway Music, Word Australia Ltd, 140 Canterbury Road, Kilsyth, Vic 3137, Australia

Word Australia Ltd, 140 Canterbury Road, Kilsyth, Vic 3137, Australia

Chord Chart

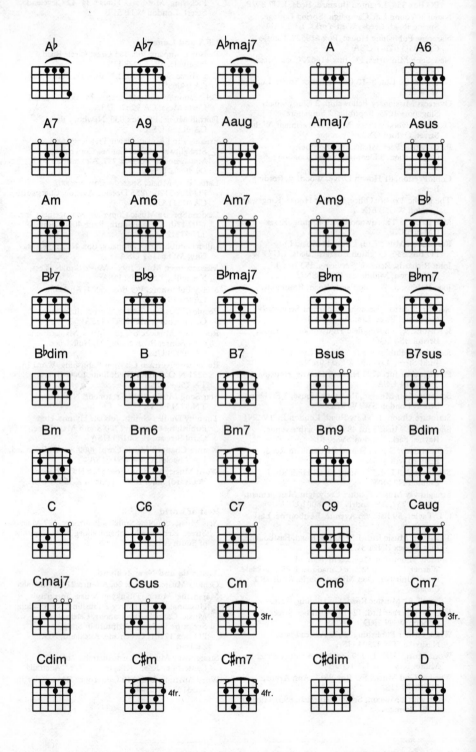

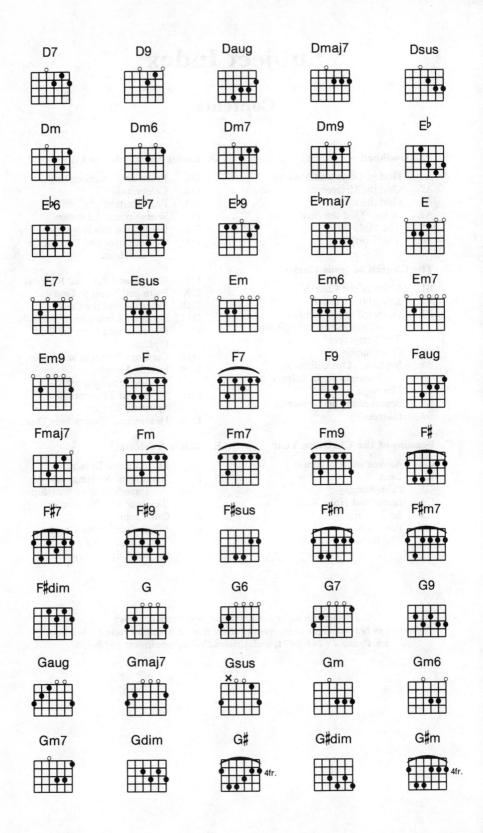

Subject Index

Contents

Titles which differ from first lines are shown in italics
Numbers in brackets refer to the number of the item in Mission Praise 1 (1–282),
Mission Praise 2 (283–647), and Mission Praise Supplement (648–758).

Section A: The Godhead

Section B: The Church of Jesus Christ

We've a story to tell 744 (261)
Who is on the Lord's side 769 (274)
Ye servants of God 784 (278)

B4. The Scriptures
Break Thou the bread of life 64 (316)
For unto us a child is born 156 (359)
For unto us a child is born 157 (665)
God is our strength and refuge 188 (372)
Let it be to me 406 (711)
Lord, Thy Word abideth 446 (486)
Master, speak! Thy servant heareth 459 (155)
O Word of God incarnate 527 (177)
Open my eyes that I may see 544 (533)
Open Thou mine eyes 546 (205)
Seek ye first the kingdom of God 590 (201)
Speak, Lord, in the stillness 608 (562)
Tell me the old, old story 628 (572)
Tell me the stories of Jesus 629 (573)
These are the facts 687 (595)

B5. Communion
Broken for me 66 (318)
Christ is risen! hallelujah 74 (322)
Father God, the Lord, Creator 130 (350)
He was pierced 222 (684)
Here from the world we turn 228
Here, O my Lord 230 (394)
I am not mine own 256 (405)
I am the Bread 260 (686)
I am the Bread of Life 261 (80)
Jesus, stand among us 380 (125)
Jesus, stand among us 381 (124)
He gave His life in selfless love 214 (387)
Let there be love 411 (137)
Let us break bread together 414 (470)
Take, eat, this is My body 622 (570)
Thank You Lord 635 (575)
Thank You Lord, for Your presence 636 (576)
There is a Redeemer 673 (590)
We break this bread 721 (750)
We come as guests invited 723 (613)
With all my heart 772 (755)

B6. Baptisms, Dedications and Presentation of Infants
All my life, Lord 17 (297)
All to Jesus I surrender 25 (4)
Because He lives 52 (18)
Fight the good fight 143 (49)
God sent His Son 52 (18)
He's got the whole wide world 225 (390)
I am not mine own 256 (405)
I have decided to follow Jesus 272 (84)
I'm not ashamed to own my Lord 323 (100)
Jesus take me as I am 382 (127)
O happy day 499 (169)
O Jesus, I have promised 501 (172)

O Saviour Christ, I now confess 519
Reign in me, sovereign Lord 570 (546)
There's a song for all the children 680
True-hearted, whole-hearted 711 (604)
When I survey the wondrous cross 755 (265)

B7. Marriage
Blessed be the tie that binds 60 (311)
In heavenly love abiding 331 (106)
Jesus, stand among us 381 (124)
Living under the shadow 423 (474)
Love divine, all loves excelling 449 (149)
O perfect Love 517 (520)
The King of love my Shepherd is 649 (221)
The Lord's my Shepherd 660 (227)

B8. Bereavement and Funerals
Abide with me 4 (2)
As we are gathered 38 (13)
Guide me, O Thou great Jehovah 201 (63)
How lovely is Thy dwelling-place 247 (399)
How lovely is Thy dwelling-place 248 (685)
I heard the voice of Jesus say 275 (85)
I will sing the wondrous story 315 (101)
I've found a friend 352 (113)
In heavenly love abiding 331 (106)
Jesus, lover of my soul 372 (120)
Join all the glorious names 392 (461)
Let saints on earth together sing 409 (466)
Like a river glorious 421 (140)
Lord, Thy Word abideth 446 (486)
My hope is built on nothing less 473 (162)
O God, our help in ages past 498 (503)
O Jesus, I have promised 501 (172)
On a hill far away 536 (175)
Peace, perfect peace 555 (184)
Rock of ages, cleft for me 582 (197)
The King of love my Shepherd is 649 (221)
The Lord's my Shepherd 660 (227)
Through the love of our God 704 (601)
Turn your eyes upon Jesus 712 (249)
When I survey the wondrous cross 755 (265)

B9. Harvest
All around me, Lord 10 (291)
All creatures of our God and King 7 (287)
All things bright and beautiful 23 (298)
All things praise Thee 24 (300)
Come, you thankful people, come 106 (333)
For the beauty of the earth 152 (356)
For the fruits of His creation 153 (52)
God of all ages 190 (669)
Great is Thy faithfulness 200 (62)
Jehovah Jireh, my provider 354 (710)
O Lord my God 506 (173)
Praise God from whom all blessings 557 (185)
The earth is the Lord's 642 (748)
We plough the fields 732 (619)
Yes, God is good 786 (640)

Section C: Seasons of the Christian Year

C1. Advent and Christmas

Angels from the realms of glory	35	(302)
Arise, shine	36	(12)
As with gladness men of old	39	(305)
At this time of giving	42	(651)
Away in a manger	47	(310)
Behold, the darkness shall cover	36	(12)
Born in the night	62	(315)
Brightest and best	65	(317)
Child in the manger	71	(657)
Christians awake	80	(325)
Come and join the celebration	83	(326)
Come now with awe	98	(655)
Come, Thou long-expected Jesus	102	(335)
Come, watch with us	105	
Cradled in a manger	107	
Darkness like a shroud	110	(658)
Ding dong! Merrily on high	114	(336)
Down from His glory	116	
El-Shaddai	119	(341)
Emmanuel	120	(342)
Emmanuel, Emmanuel	121	(659)
Faithful vigil ended	125	(660)
Fear not, rejoice and be glad	144	(47)
For unto us a child is born	156	(359)
For unto us a child is born	157	(665)
From heaven You came	162	(361)
Glory to God in the highest	177	(365)
Good Christian men, rejoice	196	(379)
Hail to the Lord's anointed	204	(64)
Hark, my soul! it is the Lord	209	(381)
Hark, the glad sound	210	(385)
Hark! the herald-angels sing	211	(384)
He is born, our Lord and Saviour	216	(676)
Holy child, how still You lie	236	(683)
I cannot tell	266	(83)
In the bleak mid-winter	337	(437)
Infant holy, infant lowly	342	(439)
It came upon the midnight clear	345	(442)
Joy to the world	393	(708)
Like a candle flame	420	(712)
Look to the skies	425	(717)
Love came down at Christmas	451	(489)
My soul doth magnify the Lord	479	(159)
Now dawns the Sun of righteousness	484	(722)
O come and join the dance	489	(723)
O come, all you faithful	491	(504)
O come let us adore Him	490	(165)
O come, O come, Emmanuel	493	(506)
O little town of Bethlehem	503	(509)
O what a gift	526	(176)
Oh what a mystery I see	535	(725)
On Christmas night	537	
Once in royal David's city	539	(530)
See, amid the winter's snow	588	(552)
See Him lying on a bed of straw	589	(553)
Silent night, holy night	597	(558)
Tell out, my soul	631	(215)
The first nowell	644	(580)
The light of Christ	652	(223)
This Child	690	(743)
Thou didst leave Thy throne	697	(237)
Thou who wast rich	700	
Tonight, while the world	713	(745)
Unto us a boy is born	714	(606)
We three kings of Orient are	740	(622)
What child is this	749	(624)
When He comes	752	(625)
While shepherds watched	764	(629)
Who is He, in yonder stall	767	(271)
Wonderful Counsellor	776	(633)
Wonderful Counsellor Jesus	777	(756)
You are the mighty King	791	(642)

C2. Lent

Forty days and forty nights	160	(360)
How lovely on the mountains	249	(79)
On Jordan's bank, the Baptist's cry	538	(528)

C3. Palm Sunday

All glory, laud and honour	9	(289)
Children of Jerusalem	70	
Come on and celebrate	99	(330)
Give me oil in my lamp	167	(58)
Hosanna, hosanna	242	(682)
Lift up your heads	418	(473)
Make way, make way	457	(491)
Ride on, ride on in majesty	580	(547)
Swing wide the gates	621	(733)
We cry hosanna, Lord	725	(615)
You are the King of glory	790	(279)

C4. Easter and Holy Week

All heaven declares	14	(649)
All you that pass by	26	
Alleluia, alleluia, give thanks	30	(9)
At Your feet we fall	45	(308)
Because He lives	52	(18)
Beneath the cross of Jesus	55	(20)
Christ is risen! hallelujah	74	(322)
Christ the Lord is risen today	76	(324)
Christ triumphant	77	(28)
Come and see, come and see	85	
Come see the beauty of the Lord	100	(331)
Father, never was love so near	138	(663)
For this purpose	155	(358)
From heaven You came	162	(361)
Give me a sight, O Saviour	166	(57)
God sent His Son	52	(18)
Hail, Thou once despised Jesus	203	(383)
Hallelujah, my Father	206	(66)
He gave His life in selfless love	214	(387)
He is Lord	220	(69)
He was pierced	222	(684)
Hévénu shalom	231	(396)
His hands were pierced	232	(70)
I am not mine own	256	(405)
I am the Bread of Life	261	(80)
I cannot tell	266	(83)
I know that my Redeemer lives	278	(86)
I live, I live because He is risen	282	(415)
I serve a risen Saviour	295	(94)
I stand amazed in the presence	296	(421)
I will sing the wondrous story	315	(101)
I'm special	325	(431)
In the cross of Christ I glory	338	(107)
In the name of Jesus	339	(109)
In the tomb so cold	340	(438)

Section D: Living the Christian Life

D3. Proclamation

D4. Worship and Adoration